# MOLECULAR PHYSICS IN PHOTOSYNTHESIS

A Blaisdell Book in the Pure and Applied Sciences

CONSULTING EDITOR
*Paul R. Gross, Brown University*

# Molecular Physics
# in Photosynthesis

## RODERICK K. CLAYTON
*Charles F. Kettering Research Laboratory*

BLAISDELL PUBLISHING COMPANY
A DIVISION OF GINN AND COMPANY
New York · Toronto · London

*First Edition, 1965*

To
B. J., Rick, and Ann

# Preface

THE FIELD OF PHOTOSYNTHESIS embraces an exceptional blending of the sciences of biology, chemistry, and physics. Students of physics and physical chemistry will find in this area a rich example of the application of their disciplines to a biological problem. Biologists will acknowledge that a familiarity with molecular physics is needed for a critical evaluation of developments in photosynthesis.

The form of this book has therefore been guided by two objectives. One aim has been to give the student of physical science an introduction to the problems of research in photosynthesis. The other has been to provide, for the biologist who is not especially trained in physics, a descriptive account of some aspects of molecular physics as well as a review of the physical problems of photosynthesis.

Part I of this book deals with the photochemical and subsequent biochemical events in photosynthesis. In tracing the evolution of current formulations of these processes one perceives the nature of the biophysical problems that have to do with the capture and utilization of light energy. Part II is a descriptive treatment of excitation in organic molecules, of some physical and chemical properties of chlorophyll, and of the migration of excitation energy and charge in molecular aggregates. In Part III the physical aspects of photosynthesis are explored in the light of the material developed in Parts I and II.

Although the names of a few investigators have been mentioned in connection with various topics, no attempt at complete annotation has been made. The interested reader is referred to the selection of books and reviews listed in the bibliography.

This monograph is an outgrowth of two series of lectures given at Dartmouth College in the winters of 1963 and 1964. I would like to thank the scientists at Dartmouth Medical School who sponsored these lectures through the Graduate Program in Molecular Biology and the Departments of Biochemistry, Cytology, and Microbiology. The series was supported by Microbiology Training Grant No. 2G-961 (Prof. R. C. Fuller, Chairman) from the National Institutes of Health.

Thanks are due also to Drs. W. Arnold, J. Franck, H. Gaffron, D. R. Kearns, R. C. Nelson, R. M. Pearlstein, and C. B. van Niel for many helpful suggestions and stimulating comments.

Roderick K. Clayton
*Charles F. Kettering Research Laboratory*

# Contents

CONTENTS

I

# Photosynthesis

# 1. An Introduction to Photosynthesis

## 1.1 Photosynthetic Organisms and Their Pigments

PHOTOSYNTHESIS is the set of processes whereby living things use light to promote biochemical events that require energy. The quality of light that can be used in photosynthesis is limited by the nature of living matter and by the spectrum of sunlight reaching the earth's surface. Ultraviolet light below 300 m$\mu$ is largely absorbed by ozone in the upper atmosphere. The transmitted component of ultraviolet can cause damaging reactions in the protein and nucleic acid of living tissues. At the other extreme, infrared light is absorbed without useful effect by the water that permeates and surrounds living matter as well as by atmospheric water vapor. Between these limits, light that could be photosynthetically useful ranges in wavelength from about 300 m$\mu$ in the ultraviolet to about 1300 m$\mu$ in the infrared. The utilization of this spectral domain by three kinds of photosynthetic organisms is illustrated in Figure 1.1.

Examination of other forms, such as the red and the blue-green algae, shows that every part of the spectrum from 300 to 950 m$\mu$ is utilized. The region in which water has limited transparency, from about 950 to 1300 m$\mu$, appears not to be used. No organism has been discovered to have photosynthetic pigments absorbing light in that region.

Chlorophyll (henceforth abbreviated Chl) is found universally, with minor variations in its structure, in photosynthetic organisms. The predominant types of Chl in green plants and algae are Chl $a$ and Chl $b$, with absorption maxima *in vivo* at about 675 and 650 m$\mu$, respectively. The green photosynthetic bacteria possess so-called chlorobium-Chl of two kinds, one absorbing maximally at 725 m$\mu$ *in vivo* and the other at 747 m$\mu$. The bacteriochlorophyll (BChl) of purple photosynthetic bacteria exhibits absorption bands *in vivo* at about 800, 850, and 870–890 m$\mu$. When BChl is extracted from purple bacteria and dissolved in an organic solvent, it shows a single absorption band at 770 m$\mu$ in place of the bands at 800–890 m$\mu$. The multiplicity of bands *in vivo* is caused by variations in the molecular environment of the BChl. The various Chl-types also have absorption maxima (the Soret bands) in the near ultraviolet or blue

3

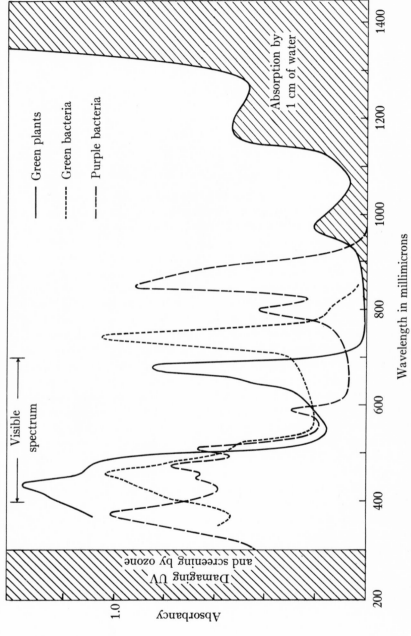

FIGURE 1.1.   Absorption spectra of three kinds of photosynthetic organisms and of 1 cm of water, showing the regions of the spectrum that can be used for photosynthesis.

region of the spectrum, and BChl has a characteristic band at 590 m$\mu$. A variant of BChl differing in its *in vitro* absorption spectrum from the "usual" BChl has been discovered in purple bacteria by K. E. Eimhjellen *et al.* The new BChl has been named BChl *b*, with the suggestion that the more common form should be called BChl *a*.

In addition to the Chl-types, carotene and other carotenoid pigments are widely (but not quite universally) distributed among green plants, algae, and photosynthetic bacteria. The carotenoids have triple-banded spectra in the region from about 400 to 550 m$\mu$. Light energy absorbed by these pigments in living cells can be transferred to Chl, and can thus be used for photosynthesis. The carotenoids also serve a protective function that will be discussed later. Another set of "accessory" pigments are the phycobilins, predominantly phycocyanin (in blue-green algae) and phycoerythrin (in red algae). Light energy absorbed by these pigments, at 500–650 m$\mu$, can be transferred to Chl and used for photosynthesis.†

In every known photosynthetic organism the conspicuous absorption band having the greatest wavelength belongs to a form of Chl. Thus Chl (or chlorobium-Chl, or BChl) provides a common denominator in two ways: it is universally present in photosynthetic organisms, and it universally produces the long-wave component in the absorption spectrum. In the evolution of photosynthetic life, the development of Chl as a catalyst for the primary photochemical events appears to have been a landmark that has remained essentially unaltered. The elaboration of different Chl-types, and of accessory pigments, may then reflect a competition for the usable regions of the spectrum. Whatever pigment absorbs light, the energy must be transferred to Chl in order to be used in photosynthesis. As we shall see later, the transfer of excitation energy among pigments is directed spontaneously toward the pigment having the longest-wave absorption band. An accessory pigment absorbing at wavelengths greater than that of the Chl-absorption band would then be worse than useless; it would act as a fruitless sink for excitation energy. This can account for the absence of natural pigments absorbing in the region 950–1300 m$\mu$.

In summary, photosynthetic organisms fall into broad categories according to their pigmentation. Higher plants contain predominantly chloro-

---

† An elegant technique was developed by T. W. Engelmann, in the nineteenth century, to measure the wavelengths of light that are effective for photosynthesis. Engelmann prepared, on a microscope slide, a mixture of filamentous algae and oxygen-seeking bacteria. The bacteria were motile only in the presence of oxygen; they tended to congregate in regions of greatest oxygen tension. After sealing the preparation so as to exclude air, Engelmann projected a microspectrum onto the preparation, along a single algal filament. In those parts of the spectrum that promoted photosynthesis, oxygen was evolved by the filament. The congregation of bacteria in these regions signaled the evolution of oxygen and thereby the occurrence of photosynthesis.

phylls $a$ and $b$ and carotenes.   In algae, ranging from multicellular forms (seaweed) to unicellular microbes, the major chlorophylls are again Chl $a$ and Chl $b$.   The greatest variety of accessory pigments is found in the algae.   The green and purple† photosynthetic bacteria contain chlorobium-chlorophylls and BChl respectively, in addition to carotenoids.   The structures and absorption spectra of Chl $a$, Chl $b$, and BChl are shown in Appendix I.

## 1.2   Earlier Biochemical Formulations of Photosynthesis

In the first quarter of this century photosynthesis was usually described by a single "over-all reaction":

$$CO_2 + H_2O \xrightarrow[\left(\substack{\text{light,} \\ \text{chlorophyll}}\right)]{} (CH_2O) + O_2. \qquad [1.2.1]$$

In this reaction $(CH_2O)$ represents a basic subunit of carbohydrate, the main product of photosynthesis that is stored in plants.   The process appeared to be a reversal of the respiratory process in which combustion of carbohydrate yields carbon dioxide and water.   The energy needed for this reversal is obtained from light absorbed by Chl.   It was conceived by R. Willstätter and others that $CO_2$ and $H_2O$, in close association with Chl, engage in a primary photochemical reaction (or set of reactions) through which the oxygen of $CO_2$ is replaced by water.   The products of such a reaction would be free oxygen and something like formaldehyde, $CH_2O$. This "photoformaldehyde" could then be converted to carbohydrate.

An entirely different conception of the chemistry of photosynthesis was introduced by C. B. van Niel in the 1930's.   The new conception stemmed from a comparison of photosynthesis in green plants and algae on the one hand and in photosynthetic bacteria on the other.

Bacterial photosynthesis differs from that of green plants and algae in two major respects, aside from the differences in pigmentation described earlier.   First, there is no evolution of oxygen attending the photosynthesis of bacteria.   Second, the bacteria will not grow photosynthetically unless they are supplied with a suitable oxidizable substance (that is, a hydrogen-donor substrate) as well as sources of carbon and nitrogen.   A great variety of organic compounds can serve as substrates, especially the simpler alcohols and organic acids.   Some photosynthetic bacteria can utilize inorganic substrates such as thiosulfate, hydrogen sulfide, and

---

† Most "purple" bacteria are actually brown or red in color, owing to the combined presence of BChl and carotenoids.   The German word *purpur* means either purple or deep red; *Purpurbakterien* was apparently translated "purple bacteria" without regard to the colors most commonly displayed.

molecular hydrogen. In many cases the transformation of the substrate in bacterial photosynthesis can be recognized as a simple oxidation of the form $H_2A \to A$. Two examples are the conversion of $H_2S$ to S and of isopropanol to acetone ($CH_3CHOHCH_3 \to CH_3COCH_3$). In cases of this kind the over-all reaction of bacterial photosynthesis could be written, at least approximately,† as

$$CO_2 + 2H_2A \xrightarrow[\text{(BChl)}]{\text{(light,)}} (CH_2O) + H_2O + 2A. \qquad [1.2.2]$$

Van Niel suggested that the photosynthesis of green plants and algae represents a special case in which water plays the role of oxidizable substrate: a case in which $H_2A$ is $H_2O$ and 2A is $O_2$. From this viewpoint the over-all reaction of green plant photosynthesis should be rewritten in the form

$$CO_2 + 2H_2O \to (CH_2O) + H_2O + O_2, \qquad [1.2.3]$$

with the implication that the evolved oxygen comes not from $CO_2$ but from $H_2O$. The correctness of this implication was established many years later through experiments with isotopic oxygen ($O^{18}$).

A parallelism between the photosynthesis of green plants and bacteria was made more convincing by H. Gaffron's investigations of hydrogen-adaptation in certain algae. Ordinarily these algae carry on a typical "green plant" photosynthesis with evolution of $O_2$. But they can be trained, through incubation with hydrogen, to perform a "bacterial" photosynthesis in which $H_2$ serves as oxidizable substrate. Under strong illumination the $H_2$-adapted algae revert quickly to the "green plant" pattern.

An important characteristic of some species of photosynthetic bacteria is their ability to grow in the dark through a typical aerobic oxidative metabolism. The substrate, $H_2A$, is oxidized by $O_2$. As a result chemical energy is made available for the synthesis of cell materials. In particular, $CO_2$ can be converted to carbohydrate in this way. In the interest of biochemical economy and unity, van Niel proposed that the reduction of $CO_2$ to $(CH_2O)$ has nothing to do with the photochemical part of photosynthesis. Having identified $H_2O$ as the substrate of photosynthetic oxygen evolution, he suggested that the primary photochemical act is a splitting of water to yield an oxidant, denoted (OH) and a reductant, denoted (H):

$$H_2O \xrightarrow[\left(\substack{\text{light,} \\ \text{Chl}}\right)]{} (H) + (OH). \qquad [1.2.4]$$

† This over-all reaction is an idealization. Cell materials other than carbohydrate may be produced, and $H_2A$ may serve, directly or indirectly, as a source of carbon in the synthesis of $(CH_2O)$ and other materials.

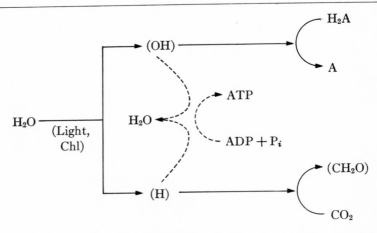

FIGURE 1.2.  *A formulation of photosynthesis according to van Niel, modified to include phosphorylation.*  $H_2A$  *is an oxidizable substrate;*  $(CH_2O)$  *represents carbohydrate.*

(H) and (OH) were not to be regarded literally as H atoms and OH radicals, but as unspecified reducing and oxidizing entities.† The primary reductant (H) could then bring about the reduction of $CO_2$ to cell materials, and the primary oxidant (OH) could be eliminated through a reaction with $H_2A$. In this formulation the details of energy storage and utilization were left unspecified. Eventually it became clear that the pyrophosphate bond of adenosine triphosphate (ATP) is an important carrier of energy in biochemical transformations, and it was demonstrated by D. I. Arnon and by A. W. Frenkel that illuminated photosynthetic tissues generate ATP from adenosine diphosphate (ADP) and inorganic phosphate ($P_i$). A simple way of inserting this information into van Niel's formulation was to allow a recombination of (H) and (OH) coupled with the phosphorylation reaction, $ADP + P_i \rightarrow ATP$. This modification imparted a certain flexibility to the scheme: any necessary proportion of reductant, (H), and chemical bond energy, as ATP, could be delivered to the biochemical machinery that generates cell materials. In this form van Niel's representation of photosynthesis is outlined in Figure 1.2.

Several aspects of van Niel's formulation have been, and still are, subjects of controversy. In its purest form the scheme provides that $H_2A$

---

† In another formalism, hypothetical substances $X$ and $Y$ interact with the primary photolytic products to form reducing and oxidizing intermediates:

$$H_2O + X + Y \xrightarrow[\left(\substack{\text{light,}\\ \text{Chl}}\right)]{} XH + YOH. \qquad [1.2.5]$$

serves only as a hydrogen-donor substrate. If this substrate is organic its oxidation may yield $CO_2$ or other carbon compounds that can be reduced in place of $CO_2$. But from the beginning of van Niel's proposals, Gaffron and others have argued that organic substrates can be assimilated by purple bacteria without being oxidized, that is, without serving as "$H_2A$." This point of view has been developed more recently by R. Y. Stanier and by H. Gest, to the extent that phosphorylation is regarded as the main fruitful activity in photosynthesis. In terms of Figure 1.2, the predominant fate of (H) and (OH) is a recombination that promotes the formation of ATP or other compounds having high-energy phosphate bonds (denoted $X \sim P$). In place of (H) as a biochemical reductant, strong reductants can be generated as needed through secondary reactions driven by ATP or $X \sim P$. A strong reductant is equivalent to an energetic electron; it is a seat of chemical energy, as is the pyrophosphate bond. In a way it does not matter whether (H) is used to form phosphate esters and thence other reductants, or whether the important stable reductants (probably reduced pyridine nucleotides) are made directly from (H). The intervention of ATP or $X \sim P$ as an energy pool will afford greater metabolic flexibility, but at the cost of some loss in thermodynamic efficiency. There is no question that phosphate esters are essential to biosynthetic processes, but it is certainly an oversimplification to maintain that (H) is used solely for phosphorylation.

Also under attack in van Niel's scheme has been the proposal that water serves as the substrate for a primary photochemical separation of oxidizing and reducing power. In alternative formulations, photo-excited Chl brings about the transfer of an electron from a donor molecule to an acceptor molecule (see Figure 1.3). In this transfer, oxidized or reduced Chl may or may not be an identifiable intermediate. Van Niel's (H) and (OH) are replaced by electrons and holes (electron vacancies). One approach to these alternatives is to say that the distinction is trivial: $H_2O$, (H), (OH), electrons, and holes are merely symbols used to denote a photochemical separation of oxidizing and reducing entities. When the

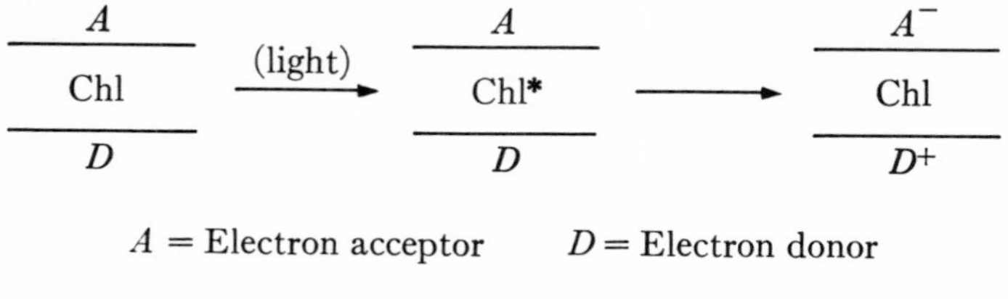

$$
\begin{array}{ccc}
\dfrac{A}{\text{Chl}} & \dfrac{A}{\text{Chl*}} & \dfrac{A^-}{\text{Chl}} \\[2mm]
\overline{D} & \overline{D} & \overline{D^+}
\end{array}
$$

$$\text{Chl} \xrightarrow{\text{(light)}} \text{Chl*} \longrightarrow \text{Chl}$$

$A$ = Electron acceptor    $D$ = Electron donor

FIGURE 1.3. *A scheme for the separation of oxidizing and reducing power at a photochemical reaction center. Excited chlorophyll (Chl\*) promotes transfer of an electron from D to A.*

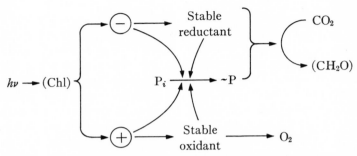

FIGURE 1.4.  *A generalization of some chemical pathways in photosynthesis illustrating the formation and utilization of oxidant and reductant, ⊕ and ⊖.*

mechanism is fully understood the symbols can be given concrete identifications with assurance.   But it can also be argued that water *is* split, in one way or another, to yield $O_2$, and that this splitting requires a concentration of energy that can only be found at the primary photochemical site.†

In following these re-interpretations of the roles of $H_2A$, (H), and $H_2O$, one can lose sight of the most significant aspect of the van Niel model: light, *via* Chl, causes a separation of oxidizing and reducing entities.   This view of the primary photochemical act is a cornerstone of current descriptions of photosynthesis.   Since its enunciation the trend of investigation has been to ask, "What are these entities, how (in physical detail) are they formed, and what (in chemical detail) does the plant do with them?"

The foregoing considerations can be summarized in a broad description of green plant photosynthesis, illustrated in Figure 1.4.

(1)  Photo-excited Chl promotes a separation of oxidizing and reducing entities (⊕ and ⊖).

(2)  These entities are converted, at least in part, to more stable oxidants and reductants.

(3)  Recombination of oxidants and reductants leads to the generation of high-energy phosphate bonds ($\sim$P) from inorganic phosphate ($P_i$).

(4)  Reductants and $\sim$P supply the reducing power and energy needed for all of the plant's activities, exemplified by the conversion of $CO_2$ to carbohydrate.

(5)  Excess oxidant is eliminated as $O_2$.   In bacterial photosynthesis $O_2$ is replaced by "oxidized substrate."

† The literature of science abounds with compelling arguments that have later been circumvented; a flexible point of view should be maintained and guided by observable phenomena.   The observable effects pertaining to primary photochemical reactions will be described in later chapters.   There is as yet no direct evidence for the participation of $H_2O$ in the primary photochemistry of photosynthesis.

## 1.3  The Evolution of Oxygen and the Reduction of Carbon Dioxide

Efforts to reproduce photosynthesis outside of the living cell have been made since the turn of the century.  The partial successes in this area have led not to a cheap way of manufacturing food but to a fuller understanding of photosynthesis *in vivo*.  The usual approach has been to break leaves in order to extract their chloroplasts and then to determine whether the chloroplast suspensions can be made to perform any of the chemical processes of photosynthesis.

The most significant single advance in the study of cell-free photosynthesis was the discovery, made by R. Hill in 1939, that illuminated chloroplasts can evolve $O_2$ provided that a suitable oxidant (that is, electron acceptor) is present.  This "Hill reaction" is promoted by such oxidants as $Fe^{+++}$, ferricyanide, quinone, and a variety of reducible dyes.  The Hill reaction appears to be a restricted case of photosynthesis in which $CO_2$ is replaced by artificial electron acceptors as ultimate recipients of photochemical reducing power.  This reaction is a light-driven transfer of electrons from $H_2O$ to the oxidant, with $O_2$ appearing as the product of the oxidation of $H_2O$.

The main significance of the Hill reaction lies in the demonstration that $CO_2$ reduction can be separated from the photochemical part of photosynthesis.  But in a different way the evolution of $O_2$ can be separated from photosynthesis, and the reduction of $CO_2$ retained.  This is the case in bacterial photosynthesis, where substrates are oxidized and no $O_2$ is evolved.  More strikingly it is the case with $H_2$-adapted algae.  In these algae $H_2$ (rather than $H_2O$) is oxidized and $CO_2$ reduced at the expense of light energy.  Thus in the Hill reaction the photochemistry is associated with $O_2$ evolution and not with $CO_2$ reduction, whereas the opposite is true for the photochemical activities of adapted algae and photosynthetic bacteria.  This means that if there is a unique photochemical event at the heart of the photosynthetic process, this event can be separated from both end results: the evolution of $O_2$ and the assimilation of $CO_2$.  Another possibility, which will be considered later, is that photosynthesis involves two different primary photochemical events.  One of these can be isolated experimentally in the Hill reaction and the other in the reaction ($H_2$ oxidation and $CO_2$ reduction) of $H_2$-adapted algae.

Through the efforts of M. Calvin, A. A. Benson, J. A. Bassham, and others, the chemistry of photosynthetic $CO_2$ reduction in algae and other phototrophs has been almost fully elucidated.  Two things are needed for this chemistry: reducing power, in the form of reduced triphosphopyridine nucleotide (TPNH), and energy in the form of ATP.  The ability of

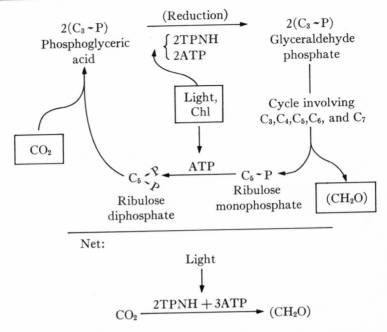

FIGURE 1.5.  *An outline of the photosynthetic carbon reduction cycle as elucidated in Calvin's laboratory.*

illuminated chloroplasts to provide these substances was demonstrated by W. Vishniac and S. Ochoa (TPNH) and by Arnon (ATP).  Frenkel has shown that bacterial chromatophores can generate reduced pyridine nucleotide and ATP in the light.

The cyclic pathway by which $CO_2$ is converted to sugar (represented as $(CH_2O)$) is outlined in Figure 1.5.  The step in which $CO_2$ is assimilated is a reaction between $CO_2$ and ribulose diphosphate (a phosphate ester of a 5-carbon sugar), leading to the formation of two molecules of phosphoglyceric acid.  This step requires neither energy nor reducing power.  The crucial light-driven step is the reduction of phosphoglyceric acid to glyceraldehyde phosphate.  This step requires the reducing power and energy of 2 TPNH and 2 ATP for the conversion of 2 molecules of phosphoglyceric acid (corresponding to the assimilation of one $CO_2$).  Through a complicated cyclic pathway, involving 4, 5, 6, and 7-carbon sugars, the six carbon atoms represented by 2 molecules of glyceraldehyde phosphate appear as one unit in sugar, $(CH_2O)$, and one molecule of the 5-carbon sugar ribulose monophosphate.  The conversion of ribulose monophosphate to ribulose diphosphate (which can react with $CO_2$, thus completing the cycle) requires one ATP.  Altogether the conversion of one $CO_2$ to

$(CH_2O)$ requires 2 TPNH and 3 ATP. The light-driven formation of 2 TPNH, and its utilization in reducing $CO_2$, represents the transfer of four reducing equivalents (for example, electrons), as does the evolution of one $O_2$ from $H_2O$. The over-all balance of atoms and electrons can be represented by the following equations, in which $TPN^+$ is triphosphopyridine nucleotide in its oxidized form.

$$2H_2O \rightarrow O_2 + 4e^- + 4H^+ \qquad [1.3.1]$$

$$2TPN^+ + 4e^- + 2H^+ \rightarrow 2TPNH \qquad [1.3.2]$$

$$2TPNH + 2H^+ + CO_2 \rightarrow 2TPN^+ + H_2O + (CH_2O) \qquad [1.3.3]$$

$$\text{Net, } CO_2 + H_2O \rightarrow (CH_2O) + O_2. \qquad [1.3.4]$$

Equation [1.3.1] should not be taken as a specific representation of the chemistry of $O_2$ evolution; it merely indicates the balance of atoms and electrons.

The ATP needed for $CO_2$ reduction is generated through phosphorylation reactions that are coupled with electron transfer processes. Two situations, called cyclic and noncyclic phosphorylation, have been distinguished. In the former, ATP formation is coupled with a recombination of primary oxidizing and reducing species and no net reducing power is stored, nor is $O_2$ evolved. In the latter the formation of ATP is coupled with electron transfer steps that attended the conversion of primary oxidant and reductant to $O_2$ and TPNH. With this degree of flexibility it is not surprising that the requisite stoichiometry, one $O_2$:2 TPNH:3 ATP, can be maintained (as was shown in Arnon's laboratory).

As was mentioned earlier, an additional degree of flexibility is afforded by the process of reductive dephosphorylation: the formation of strong reductant, such as TPNH, at the expense of phosphate bond energy. But to say that all of the TPNH used in photosynthesis is formed by this indirect route is an extreme statement.

The intervention of TPNH in the photosynthetic reduction of $CO_2$ has not been proved decisively, and there have been suggestions (especially by J. Franck) that the conversion of phosphoglyceric acid to glyceraldehyde phosphate is part of a primary (two-step, two-quantum) photochemical reaction involving Chl as a chemical participant. This idea arose from an attempt to explain the specificity of Chl in photosynthesis. It was defended on the grounds that phosphoglyceric acid is much more abundant than TPNH in photosynthesizing cells. A molecule of phosphoglyceric acid should therefore be by far the more likely to collide and react with photo-excited Chl. Of course this argument takes no account of the possibility that the reaction sequence will be determined by fixed structural associations of molecules and not by random collisions. Meanwhile there is satisfying evidence that the cycle of $CO_2$ reduction is driven only indirectly by light energy, and more directly by TPNH. The efficient photochemical reduction of pyridine nucleotide has been demonstrated in intact cells of algae and purple bacteria as well as in chloroplasts and cell extracts. Moreover the $CO_2$ reduction cycle has been shown to operate in nonphotosynthetic organisms (chemo-autotrophic and also heterotrophic bacteria). In these organisms "dark" chemical processes generate the necessary ATP and reduced pyridine nucleotide. Finally, it has been shown in Arnon's laboratory that photosynthetic formation and utilization of TPNH can be separated in time. If chloroplasts are illuminated in the absence of $CO_2$ the utilization of TPNH and ATP is blocked and these substances accumulate. In a subsequent period of darkness the reduction of added $CO_2$ will take place at the expense of the TPNH and ATP that had been formed in the light. In all likelihood then, reduced pyridine nucleotide is an important stable reductant in photosynthesis. This is not to say that reduced pyridine nucleotide is the *earliest* stable reductant to be formed.

## 1.4   The Photosynthetic Unit

Approximately 8 quanta of light absorbed by Chl suffice (see Chapter 2) for the reduction of one $CO_2$ molecule and the evolution of one $O_2$ molecule in photosynthesis. If every Chl molecule in a plant can react photochemically to generate products that are used in photosynthesis, a sufficiently intense flash of light should bring about the reduction of one $CO_2$ and the evolution of one $O_2$ for every eight Chl molecules present. This should be the result of exciting every Chl molecule, provided that the "dark" chemical machinery can cope efficiently with the flood of primary photoproducts released by the flash. In 1932 R. Emerson and W. Arnold explored this point with the green alga *Chlorella*, measuring the $O_2$ evolved in response to brief ($\sim 10^{-5}$ sec) flashes of light. These experiments showed that the maximum yield per flash was about one $O_2$ evolved for every 2500 Chl molecules present, a value three hundred fold less than one $O_2$ per eight Chl. This limiting value was attained with flashes far too weak to excite all of the Chl, and the efficiency remained about 8 quanta per $O_2$ as long as light-saturation was not exceeded.† Successive flashes could have their full effect only if they were separated by dark ("recovery") intervals of at least 0.04 sec.

From the experiments of Emerson and Arnold it could be inferred that in *Chlorella* a set of 2500 Chl molecules serves a single machine for reducing $CO_2$ and evolving $O_2$, and that 8 quanta absorbed anywhere in the set can make this machine operate once, to reduce a single $CO_2$ molecule and

† A saturating amount of light is one sufficient to produce the maximal or limiting effect, in this case a yield of one $O_2$ per 2500 Chl.

produce one $O_2$ molecule.   The machine, set in motion by the collective action of 8 quanta, requires about 0.04 sec to complete its cycle of operation.   During this time any quanta absorbed in excess of the eight requisite ones are wasted.

Stated differently, *Chlorella* (and photosynthetic organisms generally) contains photosynthetic units.   Each unit consists of a chemical reaction center served by an "antenna" of light-harvesting Chl molecules.   Quanta of energy absorbed anywhere in the light-harvesting ensemble produce unstable photoproducts of lifetime much less than 0.04 sec.   These primary photoproducts are collected efficiently, during their lifetime, by the reaction center.   There they are converted into the first stable products of photosynthesis.   A single reaction center, having collected the requisite amount of primary photoproducts, can generate its stable product in about 0.04 sec.

The (hypothetical) size of a photosynthetic unit depends on an assumption as to the number of light quanta that are needed to build a stable product.   If the earliest stable product is manifested by the complete assimilation of $CO_2$ and the evolution of $O_2$, then the reaction center must somehow combine the effects of 8 quanta in a coordinated reaction.   On that basis the unit in *Chlorella* would contain 2500 Chl molecules.   But in terms of van Niel's formulation the first chemical act in photosynthesis is the splitting of $H_2O$ to yield (H) and (OH).   Four units of (H) can reduce one molecule of $CO_2$ to $(CH_2O)$, and 4 units of (OH) can yield one $O_2$ molecule.   This means that 2 quanta are needed for a single photolytic act:

$$H_2O \xrightarrow{2h\nu} (H) + (OH), \qquad\qquad [1.4.1]$$

corresponding to the requirement of 8 quanta per $O_2$.   If (H) and (OH) can be transformed into stable reducing and oxidizing entities, these can be used at leisure for the ensuing reactions of photosynthesis.   In that case the reaction center executes a two-quantum reaction to form the first stable products, and the size of the photosynthetic unit (as defined by the flashing light experiments) is reduced by a factor of four.   Instead of a set of 2500 Chl molecules delivering the effect of 8 quanta to a reaction center, about 600 Chl molecules serve a two-quantum reaction center. And with further elucidation of partial reactions in photosynthesis (see Chapter 2) it has become conceivable that stable products are formed through "one-electron-transfer" reactions driven by single quanta of energy.   As a result the photosynthetic unit is now described most commonly in terms of a "one-quantum" reaction center served by 300 Chl molecules.

The question, "How does a photosynthetic unit operate?" is equivalent to the question, "What is the nature of the short-lived primary photoproducts that are collected by a reaction center?" This was a difficult question in the 1930's, when the photosynthetic unit first commanded serious attention. Relatively little was known about the physics of molecular interactions, so that the possibility of efficient migration of excitation energy in an ensemble of Chl molecules was generally ignored or discounted. Mechanisms involving the diffusion of chemical species (such as OH radicals) were entertained, but these led to serious difficulties in the realms of kinetics and chemical specificity. Investigators began to rationalize the photosynthetic units out of existence, but over the years the evidence for these units became more and more impressive. At the same time it became clear that the transfer of electronic excitation energy, in an ensemble of Chl molecules, could provide a sensible basis for the functioning of a photosynthetic unit. On that basis the short-lived primary photoproduct is simply a quantum of excitation in Chl. Another proposal, developed mainly by Arnold, has been that optically excited electrons and the corresponding positive holes migrate in a set of Chl molecules, in a manner typical of semiconductors. We shall see that plant tissues containing Chl do behave like organic semiconductors, exhibiting evidence for photo-ionization and migration of charge. However, these processes appear to be too inefficient to support the operation of a photosynthetic unit. At this writing the migration of energy quanta affords a completely acceptable basis (and apparently the only acceptable basis) for the operation of a photosynthetic unit.

Other lines of evidence supporting the existence of photosynthetic units can now be listed. Soon after the experiments of Emerson and Arnold, a theoretical argument was advanced by Gaffron and K. Wohl, showing that the primary effects of excitation in many Chl molecules must converge to a smaller number of reaction centers. Gaffron and Wohl computed that a single Chl molecule in a dimly illuminated plant will absorb a quantum of light only once in several minutes. At this rate an hour would elapse before a molecule of Chl could assemble the 8 quanta needed for evolution of one $O_2$ molecule. Nevertheless, when a plant is illuminated the maximal rates of $CO_2$ assimilation and $O_2$ evolution are established almost immediately. It must be concluded that energy harvested in a large set of Chl molecules is collected at a reaction center.

There is also chemical and physical evidence for photosynthetic units in plants. As we shall see later, certain molecular species have become implicated as components of a photochemical reaction center. Among these are cytochrome and a substance that appears to be a specialized form of Chl. Light absorbed by the major component of Chl promotes efficient oxidation of these "reaction center molecules"—single electron transfers apparently being driven by the energy of single quanta. In nice agreement with the size of a photosynthetic unit as determined from the flashing light experiments, there is one molecule of light-reacting cytochrome and one of the specialized Chl for every 300 Chl molecules (approximately) in green plants and algae. Furthermore there are herbicides such as DCMU† that inhibit photosynthesis completely at a concentration corresponding to one molecule of herbicide for every 200 Chl molecules. Also the efficiency of photosynthetic $O_2$ evolution (that is, Hill reaction activity), measured in fragments of plant tissues, declines abruptly when the fragments are broken so as to contain fewer than about 200 Chl molecules.

In photosynthetic bacteria the light-harvesting BChl system that forms a photosynthetic unit is considerably smaller than the corresponding Chl system in green plants and algae. On the basis of a reaction center that performs "one quantum" reactions, the bacterial unit contains from 30 to 60 BChl molecules, in contrast to 300 Chl molecules in green plants. This estimate is based on two sets of flashing light experiments with purple bacteria: measurement of substrate assimilation (by Arnold in van Niel's laboratory) and of photosynthetic ATP formation (by M. Nishimura in B. Chance's laboratory). The estimate is reinforced by the fact that "reaction center molecules" such as light-reacting cytochrome and specialized BChl are present, in purple bacteria, to the extent of one molecule for every 30–40 molecules of light-harvesting BChl.

The morphology of photosynthetic tissues is consistent with the foregoing considerations, but adds little to the structural definition of a photosynthetic unit. When purple bacteria are ruptured they release a class of subcellular particles containing all the photosynthetic pigments. These particles, termed chromatophores, can be isolated through differential centrifugation. They are roughly spherical and are from about 300 to 1000 Å in diameter. Electron micrographs of sections sliced from purple bacteria reveal spherical organelles of the same size; these seem to correspond to the isolated chromatophores. The most recent electron microscopy gives the impression that chromatophores are derived from the cell membrane through extensive invaginations of the membrane. It is not entirely clear whether the invaginations "pinch off" to form isolated spherical bodies in the cell, or whether the spherical particles are artifacts of cellular disruption. In any case the smaller chromatophores contain several hundred BChl molecules, corresponding to several photosynthetic units. Chromatophores exhibit most of the light-reactions (such as photophosphorylation) associated with photosynthesis. In green plants and in most algae the photosynthetic apparatus is contained in the large intracellular bodies known as chloroplasts. The internal structure of chloroplasts is lamellar, and in some species the lamellae exhibit discontinuities that outline smaller structures known as grana. A granum,

† 3-(3,4-dichlorophenyl)-1,1 dimethylurea.

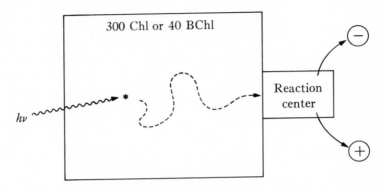

FIGURE 1.6. *Schematic representation of a photosynthetic unit and its associated reaction center. A quantum of excitation energy hv, absorbed in the light-harvesting system, migrates to the reaction center where it promotes a separation of oxidant and reductant.*

about $1\mu$ in diameter, looks like a stack of discs. It appears to be the consequence of a localized thickening that extends through several adjacent lamellae. Irrespective of the presence of grana, the lamellar surface has a rough appearance in electron micrographs, as if it were covered with hemispherical bumps about 100 Å in diameter. Each bump is of such a size as to accommodate a few hundred Chl molecules; that is, the size of a photosynthetic unit. In Calvin's laboratory the bumps have been named "quantasomes" and identified provisionally as photosynthetic units.

It was stated earlier that a cornerstone of current views on photosynthesis is the idea of a primary photochemical reaction in which separated oxidizing and reducing entities are formed (Figures 1.2, 1.3, and 1.4). A second cornerstone is the idea of a photosynthetic unit, using (in all probability) the transfer of electronic excitation energy as a mechanism by which a reaction center communicates with an antenna of light-harvesting pigment. In putting these considerations together, we are led to a model of the kind shown in Figure 1.6 as a formulation of early events in photosynthesis. In this model a single quantum of energy, absorbed anywhere in a set of 300 Chl molecules or 40 BChl molecules, migrates to a reaction center and promotes an electron-transfer event. The result is a pair of oxidizing and reducing entities that can engage in further chemical processes. If a coordinated two-quantum process occurs at the reaction center the number of Chl (or BChl) molecules in the unit should be doubled, and so forth.

# 2. Some Photochemical Reactions in Photosynthetic Tissues

## 2.1 A Photochemical Reaction Center in Photosynthetic Bacteria

WE HAVE considered a model for the initiation of photosynthesis, involving a photochemical reaction center at which oxidizing and reducing entities are formed. We have also reviewed some evidence concerning later phases of photosynthesis: the evolution of $O_2$ and the reduction of $CO_2$ at the expense of reduced pyridine nucleotide and phosphate bond energy. We are missing the details concerning the identity and pathways of interaction of the early photochemical products prior to the appearance of substances associated with the later chemical stages. In this chapter some primary photochemical reactions will be described and their potential importance for photosynthesis will be assessed.

A primary photochemical reaction in photosynthesis should have certain attributes. It should proceed more or less independently of temperature, unless the absorption of excitation energy and its migration to the photochemical reaction center is temperature-dependent. Of course, a secondary reaction coupled closely with the primary photochemical event might also be independent of temperature. The usual operational criterion is that a primary light-reaction, or a closely coupled "dark" reaction, should proceed at liquid nitrogen temperature (77°K). To be regarded with interest, a primary light-reaction should occur with high quantum efficiency, preferably in healthy tissue that can perform photosynthesis. Here a difficulty arises in that a primary photoproduct formed in healthy tissue may be utilized so rapidly that its detection is difficult. Mistreatment calculated to suppress secondary reactions may allow primary photoproducts to accumulate in easily detected amounts. But after mistreatment the observable photoproducts might be the consequences of a derailment of normal photosynthesis. They might therefore be artifacts having questionable significance as functional intermediates in the photo-

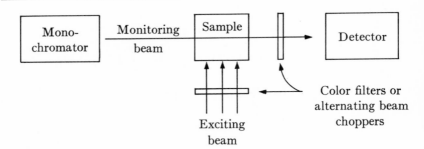

FIGURE 2.1.   *Diagram of a system for detecting light-induced absorption spectrum changes in photosynthetic tissues.*

synthetic process.   Ideally a primary photoproduct should be linked through a step-by-step reaction sequence to the major end products of photosynthesis.   This goal has not been attained with any substance that has been implicated as a primary photochemical product.

The detection of primary light-products, formed at photochemical reaction centers, has been advanced principally through differential spectrophotometry.   Light induces changes in the absorption spectra of photosynthetic tissues, and these changes can (in some cases) be correlated with reactions of known substances.   The methodology is outlined in Figure 2.1: a weak beam of monochromatic light monitors the absorbancy of a sample while a more intense beam of exciting light is applied.   Ideally the monitoring beam is too weak to cause significant excitation.   The detector is shielded from direct stimulation by the exciting beam, either through the use of complementary color filters or by a temporal alternation of excitation and measurement.   Another technique is to use steady exciting light and modulated measuring light in conjunction with a detector that responds only to modulated light.   The light-induced absorbancy changes that can be observed in photosynthetic tissues are relatively small, so that variations of the transmitted measuring light are of the order of 1% or less.   The steady component of the monitoring signal must therefore be nullified, either optically or electrically, and the smaller light-induced variations must be amplified.

Extensive application of this technique during the past decade has revealed a number of light-induced reactions in green plants, algae, and photosynthetic bacteria.   Some of these reactions can be identified chemically, and some occur with high quantum efficiency at low temperature.   We shall begin by examining a variety of light-responses in cells and chromatophores of purple photosynthetic bacteria.   Nearly all of the work in this field has been done with three types of organisms: *Rhodo-*

*spirillum rubrum, Rhodopseudomonas spheroides* and its blue-green (carotenoidless) mutants, and *Chromatium*, Strain D.

It was first shown by L. N. M. Duysens, in 1952, that the absorption
spectrum of BChl in purple bacteria is changed reversibly by illumination.
The change corresponds mainly to a bleaching of the long-wave absorption band of BChl (at 890 m$\mu$ in *R. rubrum* and *Chromatium*) and a shift
toward shorter wavelengths of a band at 800 m$\mu$. J. C. Goedheer then
showed that these effects could be brought about by chemical oxidation as
well as by light. Potentiometric titration with ferri-ferrocyanide indicated that BChl *in vivo* acts like a "one-electron" redox agent of potential
about 500 mv. It was natural to propose that oxidized BChl is an intermediate in photosynthesis. In a recent extension of these observations
(by the author in collaboration with William Arnold) it was found that the
light-induced changes in the BChl spectrum persist in films of dried
chromatophores at temperatures as low as 1°K.† These changes can
therefore be ascribed to a primary photochemical or physical electron-
transfer process.

Figure 2.2 shows a spectrum of the reversible light-induced absorbancy
changes in a dried film of chromatophores from blue-green mutant‡
*R. spheroides*, together with an absorption spectrum of the same preparation. It can be noted that the bleaching at 870 m$\mu$ is about 2.5% of the
optical density at that wavelength.

Until recently it could not be decided whether these small changes in the
BChl spectrum reflect a slight modification in the properties of all the
BChl molecules in the chromatophore or a gross alteration of relatively
few molecules. This question was settled when it was shown that most
of the BChl could be destroyed without loss of the light-reacting component. Upon prolonged incubation in the light, blue-green mutant *R.
spheroides* undergoes a spontaneous transformation in which most of its
BChl is converted to bacteriopheophytin (BPh; BChl with its Mg atom
removed). Alternatively, if chromatophores of these bacteria are treated
with detergents and illuminated in the presence of oxygen their light-
harvesting BChl (but not the light-reacting component) is destroyed.
Through a combination of these treatments it is possible to produce
chromatophores in which the only material absorbing at 870 m$\mu$ is the
light-reacting BChl component. The 870 m$\mu$ absorption band is then

---

† This temperature is attained with liquid helium in its superconducting form.
‡ The blue-green mutants of purple bacteria lack colored carotenoids. They exhibit
normal photosynthetic growth under anaerobic conditions, so the presence of carotenoids is not essential for photosynthesis. The carotenoids present in the wild type
strains exhibit light-induced absorbancy changes; this nonessential complication is
avoided when the mutants are used for spectrophotometric studies. The characteristic
light-induced change in the carotenoid spectrum is a slight bleaching and red-shift of
the absorption bands.

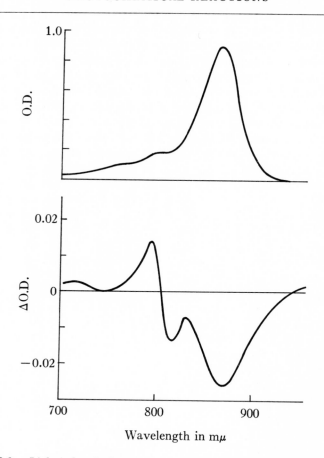

FIGURE 2.2. *Light-induced absorption spectrum changes in chromatophores of blue-green mutant Rhodopseudomonas spheroides. Upper curve: absorption spectrum. Lower curve: spectrum of the reversible light-induced changes.*

bleached completely and reversibly by light, as shown in Figure 2.3 (compare Figure 2.2). The absorption spectrum changes shown in Figure 2.2, as well as other changes to be described later, have the same size and shape in the pheophytinized, detergent-treated chromatophores as in the "fresh" material from which these chromatophores were derived. They reflect photochemical events in a specific, small component of the chromatophore, that is, in a photochemical reaction center. The light-harvesting pigment that serves this reaction center can be either BChl (in fresh material) or BPh (in the treated material). Light absorbed by BPh is utilized only half as efficiently as light absorbed by BChl, implying a partial failure in the mechanism for transferring energy to the reaction center. The reaction center component responsible for the reversible light-induced bleaching at 870 mμ has been termed P870. It can be extracted from pheophytinized chromatophores by means of organic solvents; in its extracted form it appears to be nothing but BChl. In fresh cells of *R. spheroides* there is one molecule of P870 for approximately every forty molecules of "ordinary" light-harvesting BChl.

In *R. spheroides* the absorption maximum of P870 and the long-wave absorption maximum of BChl are at 870 mμ. In *R. rubrum* and *Chromatium* these maxima are at 880–890 mμ; the light-reacting component has

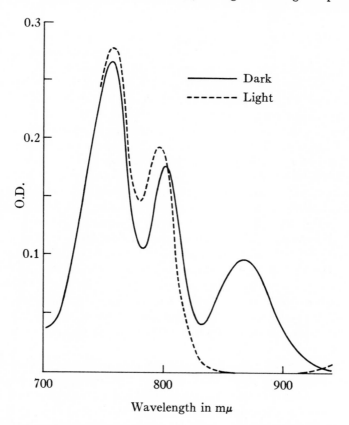

FIGURE 2.3. *Absorption spectrum of blue-green mutant R. spheroides chromatophores after treatment to convert the major BChl component to bacteriopheophytin (see text). The bands at 760 and 800 mμ are due mainly to the pheophytin; the 870 mμ band represents the light-reacting pigment P870. The dashed curve shows the spectrum of the preparation in the presence of a beam of exciting light. The difference between the solid and dashed curves represents the light-induced change; it has the form shown in Figure 2.2.*

accordingly been designated P890. The identity of P890 as a reaction center component in *R. rubrum* was inferred, by W. J. Vredenberg and Duysens, from observations of the kinetics of BChl fluorescence during the light-induced bleaching of P890.

The difference spectrum produced by chemical oxidation of chromatophores (using ferricyanide at 470 mv potential) resembles the spectrum of light-induced changes in the region of BChl absorption (as in Figure 2.2). It is the same in pheophytinized and detergent-treated. chromatophores as in fresh material. Thus the chemical effect, as well as the effect of light, is associated with P870 and not with the major BChl component.

We have seen that the light-induced bleaching of P870 corresponds, in all probability, to an oxidation in which one electron is removed. This identification is strengthened by the fact that a reducing environment accelerates the restoration of P870 after it has been bleached. An electron spin resonance (ESR)[†] signal has been detected, in Calvin's laboratory, in illuminated purple bacteria. It occurs reversibly at 77°K, and it shows a rough kinetic correspondence to the light-induced oxidation of P870.

The quantum efficiency of P870 oxidation has been computed by comparing the rate at which quanta are absorbed by BChl with the rate at which P870 is bleached. The result is that fewer than 3 quanta (perhaps one quantum), absorbed by the light-harvesting BChl in chromatophores of purple bacteria, suffice to oxidize one molecule of P870 or P890. This reasonably high quantum efficiency prevails in dried chromatophores at 1°K as well as in aqueous suspensions at room temperature.

These experiments define a photochemical unit in bacterial chromatophores. The light-harvesting part of this unit consists normally of about forty BChl molecules, but BPh will serve in place of BChl. The reaction center contains P870 or P890; this pigment appears to be BChl in a specialized environment. Energy collected by the reaction center promotes the transfer of an electron from P870 to an electron acceptor of some kind.

A number of other light-induced absorbancy changes accompany the bleaching of P870 or P890 in bacterial chromatophores. The entire spectrum of these changes is shown in Figure 2.4. Among other things it can be seen that light-induced absorption bands appear at about 435, 720, and 1250 mμ. These effects are mimicked by chemical oxidation; when induced by light they show the same kinetics as the bleaching of P870. These bands appear when P870 is bleached; they show a rough correspondence to the absorption bands of BChl at 375, 590, and 870 mμ

† The technique of ESR measurement reveals the presence of unpaired electrons in atoms and molecules. The physical significance of these electrons will be discussed in Part II of this book.

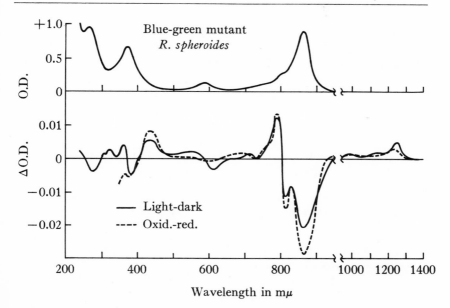

FIGURE 2.4.  *This is the same as Figure 2.2, but is extended to cover the region from 240 to 1350 mμ.  The dashed curve shows the change produced by chemical oxidation; ferri/ferrocyanide (potential 470 mv) was used for measurements above 550 mμ and KIO₄ (about 500 mv) for measurements below 550 mμ.  Changes reflecting cytochrome oxidation were eliminated in this measurement by saturating the chromatophore suspension with p-chloromercuribenzoate.*

respectively.   They have therefore been identified provisionally as components in the absorption spectrum of oxidized P870.

Another effect that can be seen in Figure 2.4 is a light-induced bleaching centered at 275 mμ.  This response is mimicked by chemical reduction rather than by oxidation.   In particular, it bears a close resemblance to the difference spectrum produced by the reduction of ubiquinone (UQ). UQ, which has been implicated as an electron carrier in nonphotosynthetic electron transport systems (that is, in mitochondria), is present in chromatophores in amounts comparable to the amount of BChl.

All of the effects shown in Figure 2.4 are seen as well in pheophytinized and detergent-treated chromatophores as in fresh material.   The oxidation of P870 implies the reduction of another substance; we have seen that this substance could be UQ.  We have thus been led to a fairly specific conception of a photochemical unit in the photosynthetic bacteria, as outlined in Figure 2.5.   In this model, constructed from the photochemical behavior of chromatophores, a primary photochemical act is the transfer of an electron from P870 to UQ.   This act occurs reversibly and efficiently

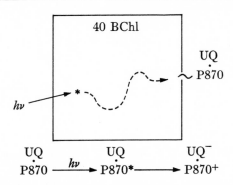

FIGURE 2.5.  *Sketch of a bacterial photosynthetic unit in which the reaction center is based on P870 (a specialized BChl molecule) coupled to ubiquinone.*

at 1°K.  Whether it is of significance in the photosynthesis of intact purple bacteria remains to be seen.

W. R. Sistrom has isolated a mutant of *R. spheroides* in which the photochemical reaction centers are defunct or missing.  The mutant cannot grow photosynthetically, but when grown aerobically in the dark it generates a normal complement of light-harvesting pigments (BChl and carotenoids).  In contrast to the parent strain grown under the same conditions, the mutant shows no reversible light-induced absorbancy changes, no light-induced ESR signal, and no transient changes in the intensity of BChl fluorescence.  Chemical oxidation of chromatophores from the mutant strain reveals no trace of P870.  Chromatophores of the parent strain catalyze a number of photochemical processes involving oxidation of external electron donors coupled with reduction of external electron acceptors (for example, oxidation of cytochrome coupled with reduction of UQ).  Chromatophores of the mutant strain do not catalyze these reactions.  These results, together with those obtained with pheophytinized chromatophores, show clearly that reaction centers containing P870 exist and are related in some way to photosynthesis.

## 2.2   Cytochromes in Bacterial Photosynthesis

Since the time of Duysens' original observations on the light-reactions of BChl (later P870 and P890), it was anticipated that cytochromes should serve an important function in the electron transport machinery of photosynthesis.  This expectation was based on the known importance of cytochromes in nonphotosynthetic electron transport and on the fact that cytochromes had been found, by Hill and his collaborators, in photosynthetic tissues.  In terms of van Niel's formulation (Figure 1.2) it was thought that cytochromes might link the primary photo-oxidant, (OH), to the oxidation of substrate.

Light-induced cytochrome (Cyt) oxidation in photosynthetic bacteria was indeed observed through difference spectrophotometry, not only by Duysens but by many others, notably the investigators† in Chance's laboratory. The characteristic spectrum of this reaction is somewhat variable, depending on the type‡ (or types) of Cyt involved. The cytochromes of photosynthetic bacteria that are oxidized by light are mainly in the category of the c type. A typical spectrum for the light-induced oxidation of a bacterial Cyt is shown in Figure 2.6.

In living cells of photosynthetic bacteria under anaerobic conditions the light-reactions shown in Figure 2.4 are nearly absent. Instead a

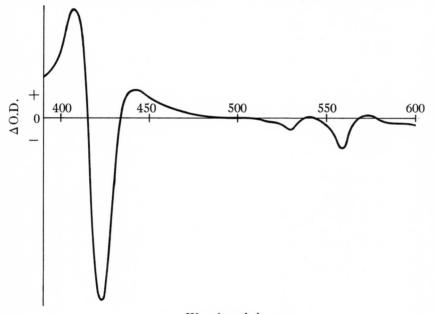

Wavelength in mμ

FIGURE 2.6. *Difference spectrum showing the light-induced oxidation of cytochrome in Chromatium chromatophores. The Soret band of the cytochrome is shifted toward shorter wavelengths (producing the changes from about 390 to 440 mμ), and the β and α bands are bleached.*

† H. and M. Baltscheffsky, M. Nishimura, J. M. Olson, J. Ramirez, and L. Smith.
‡ Cytochromes of different types can be distinguished most readily on the basis of their oxidation potentials and their absorption spectra. Classification into "types" a, b, c, et cetera has been based primarily on the location of an absorption band of the reduced Cyt in the region 550–560 mμ (the so-called alpha band).

spectrum characteristic of Cyt oxidation predominates, together with some changes associated with carotenoid pigments. It appears that the Cyt reaction is pre-eminent whenever the photo-oxidized Cyt can be reduced rapidly in the dark. This is so in anaerobic intact cells and also in chromatophores that are placed in a mildly reducing environment (such as $0.01M$ glutathione in a buffered aqueous solution). Under these conditions the reaction of P870 and most of the other effects described in Figure 2.4 are truncated or missing. Conversely, a variety of treatments† can be used to keep the cytochromes permanently oxidized and hence unable to show a reversible light-induced oxidation. The reactions of Figure 2.4 are then conspicuous.

It was mentioned earlier that the oxidation of P870 or P890 proceeds with high quantum efficiency (fewer than 3 quanta per electron-transfer) in chromatophores. This is observed only if the Cyt reaction has been suppressed. Under favorable conditions (for example, in intact cells of *Chromatium* exposed to dim light) the light-induced oxidation of Cyt has been shown (by J. M. Olson) to proceed with the ideal efficiency of one quantum per electron transfer. Freshly prepared chromatophores of *R. spheroides* exhibit efficient light-induced Cyt oxidation in dim light and show the oxidation of P870 only at exciting light intensities sufficient to saturate the cytochrome reaction. But after these chromatophores have been washed with distilled water the Cyt reaction is nil and the oxidation of P870 occurs efficiently in dim light. These relationships are sketched in Figure 2.7.

It was shown by Chance and Nishimura that the light-induced oxidation of Cyt proceeds efficiently at $77°K$. The reaction is irreversible at this temperature, in contrast to the reversibility of the reaction of P870 (and of the light-induced ESR signal).

The amount of light-reacting Cyt in photosynthetic bacteria is comparable to the amount of P870 or P890: about one molecule for every forty BChl molecules. The light reaction of Cyt in *R. spheroides*, like the light reactions described earlier, survives the processes of pheophytinization and detergent treatment that eliminate the light-harvesting BChl.

From the foregoing it can be seen that the oxidation of Cyt, as well as the reactions of P870 and UQ‡ should be considered among primary photo-

---

† With intact cells, aeration or application of poisons such as sodium azide maintains some cytochromes in an oxidized state. A light-induced oxidation of these cytochromes cannot then be observed. The same result is achieved in chromatophores through prolonged illumination, by repeated washing, or by drying the material. Dried films of *Chromatium* chromatophores exhibit light-induced cytochrome oxidation, but the reversal of this reaction requires several hours of darkness.

‡ It should be emphasized that the identification of UQ as the reaction-partner of P870 is tentative. It is based solely on the absorption spectrum changes around 275 m$\mu$ that accompany the photo-oxidation of P870, plus the fact that these changes in the ultraviolet are mimicked by chemical reduction and not by oxidation.

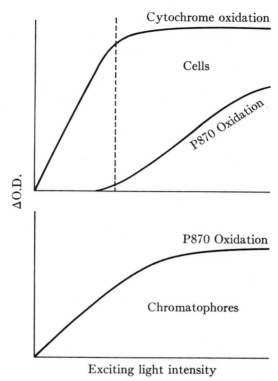

FIGURE 2.7. *Dependence of light-induced absorbancy changes in R. spheroides on the intensity of the exciting light. Upper graph: changes reflecting the oxidations of cytochrome and P870 in intact cells. Lower graph: oxidation of P870 in chromatophores. With dim exciting light the quantum requirement for cytochrome oxidation is about 1 quantum per electron transfer in the intact cells. For P870 oxidation in chromatophores the requirement is about 2 quanta per electron transfer.*

chemical events that occur at reaction centers. That a single reaction center contains UQ, P870, and Cyt is suggested by the preservation of these substances (and their reactions) in pheophytinized chromatophores, and also by the equimolar concentrations of P870 and light-reacting Cyt. This does not mean, of course, that the oxidations of Cyt and P870 and the reduction of UQ are all a part of the initiation of photosynthesis. The question of the functionality of these reactions will be deferred for the moment.

At this point a digression suggests itself, into the problem of the essentiality of Chl (or BChl) for photosynthesis. In most plants, algae, and photosynthetic bacteria, the major light-harvesting pigment is Chl in one form or another.    This does not mean that Chl is uniquely suited to the role of light-harvesting pigment.    Accessory pigments (for example, carotenoids and phycobilins) abound in photosynthetic organisms; light absorbed by them is often used as efficiently for photosynthesis as light absorbed by Chl itself.    In chromatophores, the light-harvesting BChl can be replaced entirely by BPh without serious impairment of certain photochemical reactions.    But Chl and BChl seem to be irreplaceable as initiators of the chemistry of photosynthesis.    BChl is present, in the form of P870, as a photo-oxidizable component of a reaction center.    Green plants and algae contain a corresponding substance, called P700, which appears to function at a reaction center in an electron-transferring capacity.    These considerations suggest that Chl and BChl are *essential* for photosynthesis only as "photo-electron-transfer" agents in reaction centers.    Perhaps the most primitive photosynthetic organisms had no light-harvesting system at all, other than the "reaction center Chl" itself. But from the calculations of Gaffron and Wohl (see Section 1.3), the elaboration of a light-harvesting antenna would introduce an enormous selective advantage.    Since Chl was already in use at the reaction center, the simplest way to build an antenna would have been to make more of this pigment.    The development of accessory pigments could then have resulted from a competition for unused parts of the spectrum.    The green plants and algae, being more advanced than the purple bacteria, have elaborated a larger antenna and a greater diversity of accessory pigments.

To return to a description of photochemical reaction centers in bacterial chromatophores: we have seen that the light-reactions of Cyt, P870, and UQ occur in preparations that have lost their light-harvesting BChl.    In addition to these "natural" reactions, L. P. Vernon and others have studied a variety of artificial electron-transfer reactions that are promoted by illuminated chromatophores.    Among these is the interesting case (described by Vernon and W. S. Zaugg) in which the oxidation of mammalian Cyt *c* is coupled photochemically with the reduction of externally added UQ. This reaction is effected by pheophytinized chromatophores as well as by fresh ones, at rates commensurate with the amount of P870 and the effectiveness of the light-harvesting system (BChl or BPh).    This and other artificial reactions are therefore dependent on reaction centers, and not on local photochemistry in the major BChl component.

A final and elegant demonstration of the significance of reaction centers in bacterial photosynthesis is afforded by the properties of the nonphotosynthetic mutant of *R. spheroides* isolated by W. R. Sistrom and described in the preceding section.

The oxidation of Cyt and the appearance of $(P870^+, UQ^-)$† display a competitive aspect, in that the latter reaction is conspicuous only when the

† The expression $(P870^+, UQ^-)$ will be used to connote oxidized P870 and reduced UQ, as implicated by the nature of the appropriate light-induced absorbancy changes.

former is blocked. These reactions appear to be different manifestations of events in a single reaction center, and we must consider whether they both have significance in the initial photochemistry of photosynthesis. Appearance of ($P870^+$, $UQ^-$) is a reaction, involving a specialized BChl molecule, that occurs efficiently and reversibly at low temperatures. These properties suggest that the formation of ($P870^+$, $UQ^-$) represents the first photochemical electron transfer act of photosynthesis. The obvious alternative is that the first act is an oxidation of Cyt coupled with reduction of an unspecified electron acceptor. The acceptor might be a specialized BChl molecule, perhaps even P870. There are several arguments in favor of the formation of ($Cyt^+$, $A^-$) as the first photochemical event in photosynthesis. The irreversibility of Cyt oxidation at low temperature is appropriate, since it implies that $Cyt^+$ is a stable photochemical product until acted on by the "dark" enzyme machinery of photosynthesis. The importance of Cyt in the enzymology of electron transport is well established. But most significantly, the oxidation of Cyt (and not the formation of ($P870^+$, $UQ^-$)) is the main observable primary event in healthy, photosynthesizing cells exposed to dim light.

Both reactions, the formations of ($P870^+$, $UQ^-$) and ($Cyt^+$, $A^-$), can be retained in the photochemical machinery of photosynthesis if they are regarded as sequential events, with oxidized P870 serving as the electron acceptor in the oxidation of Cyt:

$$P870 + UQ \overset{h\nu}{\to} P870^* + UQ \to P870^+ + UQ^-, \qquad [2.2.1]$$

followed by

$$P870^+ + Cyt \to P870 + Cyt^+. \qquad [2.2.2]$$

It is only necessary to stipulate that the second reaction follows the first very quickly. Then as long as Cyt is capable of reacting with $P870^+$, as in healthy, anaerobic intact cells, an accumulation of $P870^+$ cannot be detected. But if the Cyt is kept oxidized, as in aerated cells or washed chromatophores, the second reaction is blocked and $P870^+$ is observed as a primary photoproduct. As this interpretation would require, $UQ^-$ can be observed as a primary photoproduct whether the second reaction occurs or not.

A different point of view, advanced especially by Chance and by M. Kamen, is that the oxidation of Cyt, probably coupled with the reduction of BChl, is the primary photochemical act of photosynthesis. The formation of ($P870^+$, $UQ^-$) is an aberrant event that occurs only when Cyt is already oxidized. In this view there is no special reason to implicate UQ as a primary electron acceptor; the $BChl^-$ formed in the primary reaction could donate its energetic electron to some other molecule. Development of this hypothesis has been hampered because until very recently there has been no spectrophotometric evidence for the formation of

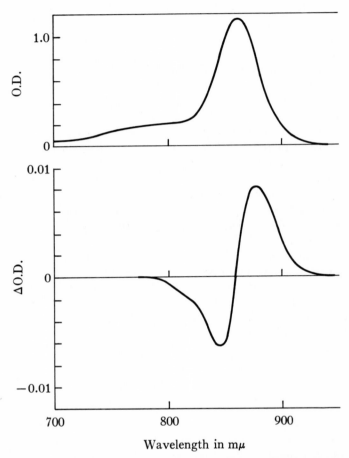

FIGURE 2.8. *Light-induced absorbancy changes in freshly harvested cells of blue-green mutant R. spheroides. The cells were suspended in 30% aqueous albumin to reduce the turbidity. Upper curve: absorption spectrum. Lower curve: spectrum of the light-induced changes.*

reduced BChl accompanying the oxidation of Cyt. This may be because the "cytochrome-oriented" investigators have tended to shun the spectral region from 750 to 950 m$\mu$. Some new spectrophotometric evidence has been observed in *R. spheroides* in the form of the light-induced change shown in Figure 2.8. This change accompanies the oxidation of Cyt and has the same kinetics and light-saturation properties. It corresponds to a bathychromic shift (that is, toward greater wavelengths) of an absorption band coincident with the main BChl band. This component could be

P870, but there is no compelling reason to believe that it is. Circumstantial information indicates that this reaction is a manifestation of the reduction of BChl (or perhaps of P870). It has been called the $B^-$ reaction. In freshly prepared chromatophores or cells of *R. spheroides* exposed to bright exciting light, both the reactions producing (P870$^+$, UQ$^-$) and (Cyt$^+$, B$^-$) are manifested. They can then be distinguished kinetically, and it appears that P870$^+$ and B$^-$ can be formed independently and can be present simultaneously.

If one were to choose between the appearance of (P870$^+$, UQ$^-$) and (Cyt$^+$, B$^-$) as signalling "the" primary photochemical act of photosynthesis, the natural choice would be the latter because it predominates in living cells under dim light. The former reaction may then be given a secondary function or no function at all. But it remains possible that the sequence of events is described correctly in Equations [2.2.1] and [2.2.2], with B$^-$ appearing as a trivial accompaniment of Cyt oxidation. It is even possible that (P870$^+$, UQ$^-$) and (Cyt$^+$, B$^-$) reflect independent, functional photochemical acts that cooperate in the initiation of photosynthesis. Some specific formulations of these possibilities are outlined in Figure 2.9.

The green bacteria are currently being studied spectrophotometrically by J. M. Olson and collaborators. In these bacteria the only light-induced absorbancy changes that have been reported correspond to the oxidation of Cyt and the bleaching of a substance absorbing at 840 m$\mu$. Older cells, and extracts of cells, show neither a light-induced ESR signal nor any reversible absorbancy changes at wavelengths greater than 700 m$\mu$. Young, growing cultures were found to exhibit a light-induced ESR signal as well as the absorption change at 840 m$\mu$. Absorption spectra of the green bacteria show a main band at 725 or 747 m$\mu$ (depending on the species) due to chlorobium-Chl.† Beyond this band there is a much smaller band at about 805 m$\mu$. The pigment responsible for this band has been isolated and described by J. M. Olson and C. A. Romano; in organic solvents it has the same absorption spectrum as BChl. The substance responsible for the reversible bleaching at 840 m$\mu$ could also be BChl, analogous to P870 in purple bacteria. There is some evidence that the 805 m$\mu$-absorbing pigment acts as an energy sink in conjunction with a reaction center in the green bacteria. For example, light absorbed by this pigment appears to be at least as efficient as light absorbed by chlorobium-Chl in promoting the oxidation of Cyt.

If the reaction center in green bacteria does utilize BChl, an interesting evolutionary pattern can be visualized: A primordial photosynthetic

---

† There are two known types of chlorobium-Chl, designated by numerical suffixes "650" and "660" according to the location of the main long-wave absorption band of the pigment in ether.

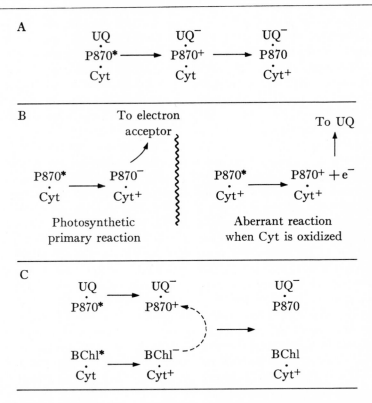

FIGURE 2.9. *Three hypotheses for the primary photochemical events in bacterial photosynthesis. Detailed discussion in the text.*

bacterium functioned by means of BChl in a photochemical reaction center. It then developed a light-harvesting antenna of BChl (in the case of purple bacteria) or of chlorobium-Chl (in the green bacteria). The survival value of an antenna of chlorobium-Chl can be appreciated by reference to Figure 1.1. It enables the green bacteria to grow under a layer of purple bacteria, in light that has been robbed of its 800–900 m$\mu$ component.

## 2.3  Some Primary Reactions in Green Plants and Algae

Differential spectrophotometry has proved to be more difficult in chloroplasts and algae than in purple bacteria, probably because of a tenfold greater preponderance of inert pigments over the light-reacting substances. Moreover, the kinetic patterns of light reactions in green plants and algae are more complex than those in purple bacteria. This results from a fact that must be anticipated here: that the photosynthesis of green plants and algae involves the cooperation of two distinct photochemical reactions. At this point we shall examine a few manifestations of primary reactions in green plant chloroplasts and algae. The possible significance of these phenomena will become clearer in the context of the next two chapters, when the question of two light reactions is explored.

As with the purple bacteria, the observation of light-induced absorbancy changes in algae was initiated by Duysens, who showed (among other things) that a substance similar to Cyt $f$ becomes oxidized in illuminated *Porphyridium*. This and other findings were confirmed and extended in B. Kok's laboratory. Kok's chief contribution was the observation and characterization of P700, a pigment that appears to be the counterpart of the bacterial pigments P870 and P890. P700 is a trace-constituent of green plant chloroplasts and algae; it has an absorption band at about 705 m$\mu$ (that is, about 30 m$\mu$ beyond the main long-wave band of Chl *a in vivo*). P700 is bleached reversibly by light, and this bleaching corresponds to an oxidation of the pigment. Chemical titration shows P700 to be a "one-electron" redox agent whose potential is about 450 mv. An ESR signal has been correlated with the oxidation (by light or by ferricyanide) of P700 in chloroplasts. The photochemical oxidation of P700 *in vivo* is coupled with oxidation of Cyt $f$; a primary electron acceptor associated with these events has not been identified with certainty. Extraction of chloroplasts with acetone-water mixtures removes Chl $a$ but not P700; in this way the ratio of P700 to Chl $a$ has been increased sevenfold. After extraction the chloroplasts retain the light reaction of P700, but not the reaction of Cyt $f$. In such material it can be seen that a light-induced bleaching at 430 m$\mu$ accompanies the bleaching at 705 m$\mu$.

The bleaching at 430 m$\mu$ strengthens an identification of P700 as a specialized molecule of Chl $a$, serving as an energy sink and an initiator of photochemistry in a photosynthetic unit. By assuming that the extinction coefficient of P700 is the same as that of Chl $a$, it can be computed that there is one molecule of P700 and one of Cyt $f$ for roughly 300 molecules of Chl $a$ in chloroplasts. Kok reports that one quantum absorbed by Chl $a$ suffices for the bleaching of one P700 molecule. It seems appropriate, then, to regard P700 as a "reaction-center Chl" in green plants and algae. Energy is absorbed by light-harvesting Chl $a$ and collected by P700; as a result an electron is transferred from P700 to an acceptor molecule. One may then speculate (and there is evidence to support this speculation; see later in this section) that the photo-oxidized P700 regains an electron from Cyt $f$, in analogy with the corresponding speculation about P870 and bacterial Cyt.

W. L. Butler has detected a pigment resembling P700 in bean leaves and other green tissues on the basis of its absorption and fluorescence; the fluorescence (at about 720 m$\mu$) is greatly intensified at 77°K. Butler's pigment acts as an energy sink for light absorbed by Chl $a$. Several other long-wave forms of Chl $a$ have been observed, especially in C. S. French's laboratory. An example is the component in *Euglena* absorbing at 695 m$\mu$. This pigment does not appear to engage in a reversible photochemical reaction. Identification of a long-wave Chl as "P700" should be based on its reversible photo-oxidation, or at least on its ability to collect light energy absorbed by the major Chl component. At present it is not certain that the total amount of P700 is given by the extent of the reversible light-induced bleaching. Possibly there is a larger pool of this material, with only a small fraction bleached in the illuminated steady state.

To date, the most detailed spectrophotometric investigation of chloroplasts has been conducted in H. T. Witt's laboratory. A number of interrelated light reactions have emerged; these have been described in highly condensed research communications and incorporated into formulations that continue to grow in complexity. Most of these observations will be described later, when they can be fitted into schemes that account for the cooperation of two photochemical reactions. Only a few observations relating to P700 and Cyt $f$ will be considered here.

Witt and collaborators showed that P700 and Cyt $f$ in chloroplasts are oxidized by illumination, reversibly at room temperature and irreversibly at about 120°K. The irreversibility of P700 oxidation at low temperature stands in contrast to the reversibility of P870 oxidation in bacterial chromatophores. Correspondingly, the ESR signal associated with P700 oxidation is irreversible at low temperature, whereas the ESR signal in purple bacteria remains reversible. Especially interesting are the kinetics reported by Witt *et al.*, for the reactions of P700 and Cyt $f$ at room temperature. A brief flash of light (about $10^{-5}$ sec) elicits a change at 705 m$\mu$, corresponding to P700 oxidation, that decays in about $10^{-3}$ sec. The onset of Cyt $f$ oxidation is not an immediate response to the flash; instead it parallels the decay of the P700 reaction. It would appear that light displaces an electron from P700 to an acceptor and that an electron subsequently moves from Cyt $f$ to P700. At low temperature both components become and remain oxidized.

Due to experimental difficulties these kinetic data are marginally convincing. If they can be believed they indicate that the behavior of P700 and Cyt $f$ corresponds to the possibility proposed in Figure 2.9A for the reactions of P870 and Cyt in chromatophores. The "fast" kinetics of the reactions of P870 and Cyt in purple bacteria have not yet been measured.

Reduced pyridine nucleotide has been implicated, as mentioned earlier, as an intermediate in the reduction of $CO_2$. Its formation in illuminated photosynthetic tissues has been reported frequently, but not as the direct product of a primary photochemical act.    For one thing the photochemical reduction of pyridine nucleotide in chloroplast suspensions is mediated by another electron carrier, A. San Pietro's photosynthetic pyridine nucleotide reductase (PPNR, or ferredoxin).    In turn, there is no evidence to indicate that PPNR is a direct electron acceptor in a primary photochemical reaction.

# 3. The Cooperation of Two Quanta or Two Light Reactions in the Photochemistry of Photosynthesis

## 3.1 The Quantum Efficiency of Photosynthesis

IN THE preceding chapter a description of primary photochemical events was rendered without regard for the occurrence of two distinct photochemical events in green plants and algae. We shall now trace the development of "two-quantum" theories of photosynthesis, returning gradually to the present ideas regarding two distinct light reactions. In this framework it will be possible to discuss primary photochemical reactions in greater detail.

The energetics of photosynthesis involves light quanta whose energy can be expressed in units of electron volts, or as wavelength or wave number. Energy exchange in chemical processes is usually described in units of kcal/mole. For convenience the equivalence of these units is shown in Figure 3.1. Thus one quantum of 675 m$\mu$ light (wave number 14,800 cm$^{-1}$) has an energy of 1.84 ev, and a gram-mole of such quanta (that is, one einstein, or $6.02 \times 10^{23}$ quanta) has an energy of 42 kcal.

When the first chemical step in photosynthesis was formulated as a light-induced separation of reducing and oxidizing equivalents it became possible to think concretely about the meaning of quantum efficiency. The reduction of $CO_2$ to $(CH_2O)$ and the evolution of $O_2$ are processes that involve the transfer of four electrons per molecule. In terms of a primary light reaction such as

$$H_2O \xrightarrow{h\nu,\ Chl} (H) + (OH) \text{ or } (Chl, h\gamma) \rightarrow \ominus + \oplus, \qquad [3.1.1]$$

the primary reaction must occur at least four times, yielding four reducing equivalents and four oxidizing equivalents, to afford the assimilation of one $CO_2$ and the evolution of one $O_2$ molecule. If the primary reaction is

38

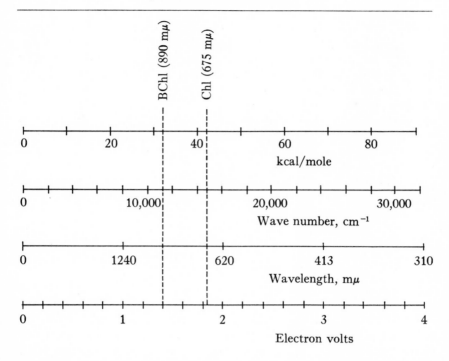

FIGURE 3.1. *The equivalence of four measures of energy commonly used in photo-chemistry. The energies of light quanta at the long wave absorption maxima of Chl and BChl in vivo are shown.*

driven by a single quantum, the quantum requirement for photosynthesis should be at least 4 quanta per $CO_2$. If the primary reaction is a coordinated two-quantum event the requirement should be 8 $h\nu/CO_2$, and so forth.

The introduction of water splitting in the primary photochemical act seems at first sight to pose a special energetic problem. The energy of an O—H bond in water is 111 kcal/mole, or 4.8 ev. To break this bond in an isolated $H_2O$ molecule would require the energy of at least 3 quanta of light absorbed by Chl (at about 675 m$\mu$). But if the $H_2O$ molecule is in contact with other substances ($X$ and $Y$) having affinity for (H) and (OH), the dissociation energy can be much smaller than 111 kcal/mole. A reaction of the form

$$H_2O + X + Y \xrightarrow{h\nu, \text{ Chl}} XH + YOH \qquad [3.1.2]$$

could in principle be driven by the energy of a single quantum. From this point of view the splitting of water entails no special energy problem.

Why, then, should water be put explicitly into models of a primary photochemical act? One answer seems to be "because it is there." As a substrate for photochemistry, water can surely be present at a satisfyingly high concentration. But any other substance will have a high local concentration if it has been incorporated into the structure of a photochemical reaction center. Another argument is that water is, after all, the source of the evolved $O_2$. But we know almost nothing about the chemistry of $O_2$ evolution, and sensible schemes can be concocted whereby water is dissociated in "dark" chemical reactions. Of the various current formulations of photosynthesis, some are written with and some without a primary photolysis of water. None of them suffers an essential change in meaning or in feasibility when water is introduced to, or withdrawn from, the primary photochemical picture. In a sense we can afford to be patient and deal with the chemistry of water as it becomes known with certainty. The photochemical reactions of Cyt, P870, and P700, proceeding as they do at low temperatures and in dried preparations, are probably electron transfer events that do not involve molecular rearrangements such as the splitting of water.

As long as photosynthesis was thought to begin with one kind of light reaction, the minimum quantum requirement was restricted to values of 4, 8, 12, . . . $h\nu/CO_2$, depending on the number of quanta involved in the primary reaction. This conclusion was the point of departure for a bitter and sustained controversy, that survives to this day, over the quantum efficiency of photosynthesis. On the basis of manometric measurements of $CO_2$ and $O_2$ exchange, accompanying the photosynthesis of the green alga *Chlorella*, O. Warburg and his collaborators (E. Negelein, D. Burk, and others) have consistently reported a quantum requirement in the neighborhood of 4 $h\nu/CO_2$, and sometimes values as small as 2.7 $h\nu/CO_2$. Other investigators, notably R. Emerson and C. M. Lewis, reported values of about 6 to 10 $h\nu/CO_2$. The vigor with which Warburg defended his results, and also the great potential significance of the outcome, drew dozens of investigators into an examination of this discrepancy. As a result the quantum efficiency of photosynthesis became perhaps the most exhaustively measured phenomenon in the history of science. The measurements by Warburg *et al.*, extend from 1922 to the present; the past twenty-five years have seen dozens of investigations in laboratories other than Warburg's. The outcome of all this effort is that only Warburg and his colleagues could observe a requirement of 4 $h\nu/CO_2$ or less. The consensus of all other investigators is that from 6 to 10 quanta are needed. The non-Warburg school maintains that Warburg's low quantum requirements are attributable to induction phenomena: the measurements had been made while the algae were in a transitory state of imbalance with regard to the stoichiometry of $CO_2$ uptake and $O_2$ evolution. Warburg's rebuttal is that the measurement of "true" quantum efficiency is an exquisite art; the algae must be treated in special ways if they are to exhibit the high efficiency of which they are capable. The development of this art came, over the years, through progressive refinements in technique. It must be concluded that Warburg was remarkably fortunate to have obtained values less than 4 $h\nu/CO_2$ early in his career, before the art was consciously refined.

The most outspoken opponents of Warburg's position have.been Franck, Gaffron, and E. Rabinowitch. Their criticism has been based most forcefully on the restrictions imposed by thermodynamics and the quantization of energy. By taking 4 and 8 quanta as alternatives for the minimum number needed to reduce one $CO_2$ molecule through a reaction of the form of Equation [3.1.1], one can compile an energy budget to see whether 4 quanta could possibly suffice. If not, the value of 8 quanta should (in these terms) be accepted. Wohl, Franck, and others have conducted such calculations, starting with the fact that the free energy of one equivalent of $(CH_2O)$, as sugar, is 118 kcal greater than that of one mole of $CO_2$. In the initial photochemical act, an energy barrier of some kind must exist to prevent an immediate recombination of primary reductant and oxidant. The height of this barrier must be somewhat greater than the energy of the metastable species (reductant and oxidant) formed in the primary act. The amount of energy lost in surmounting this barrier is probably at least 0.3 ev per quantum, or 28 kcal/mole of $CO_2$.† Any sensible assumption about the chemistry of $O_2$ evolution entails a loss of at least 20 kcal/mole. Other losses, such as those attending the formation and utilization of ATP, can be estimated conservatively to be 18 kcal/mole. Upon adding all of these energy requirements, at least 184 kcal are needed for the assimilation of one mole of $CO_2$ and the evolution of one mole of $O_2$. The energy provided by 4 einsteins of light at 675 m$\mu$ is 168 kcal, which is insufficient. If we must choose between four and eight as the minimum quantum requirement for photosynthesis, we are thus led to the latter figure. This is what is meant by the now classical statement that 2 quanta are needed in order to break an O—H bond in water so as to produce a reductant capable of reducing $CO_2$ to sugar and an oxidant at the level of $O_2$.

One consequence of these computations is that Warburg and Burk have abandoned the van Niel formulation (and its modern outgrowths and counterparts) in favor of something resembling the older photochemical theories of Willstätter and others: a concerted photochemical act that

---

† If the primary photochemical act is mediated by a triplet excited state of Chl (see Chapter 8), the loss is 0.4 ev per quantum. And if the primary reductant and oxidant are in an aqueous environment they cannot differ in energy by more than 1.2 ev without becoming involved in a wasteful electrolysis of water. In that case a loss of 0.6 ev per quantum is inevitable.

occurs in a complex of Chl, $CO_2$, and $H_2O$. The development of this theory, and its tenuous experimental basis, has been described elsewhere[†] and will not be pursued here.

About ten years ago, then, the primary photochemical act of photosynthesis was thought by most investigators to be something like

$$H_2O \overset{2h\nu}{\rightarrow} (H) + (OH), \qquad [3.1.3]$$

and an elucidation of this act was sought in terms of physical mechanisms whereby two quanta could be brought together in a cooperative reaction at a single photochemical site.   The evolution of such efforts will be discussed after some physical background has been developed.   We shall turn now to the emerging identification of two independent photochemical reactions in green plant photosynthesis.


## 3.2   The Enhancement Phenomenon and Its Implications

In the early 1950's, when Duysens, French, L. R. Blinks, F. Haxo, and others were studying the efficiency of energy transfer from accessory pigments to Chl $a$ in algae, a paradox became evident.   Light absorbed by some accessory pigments was found to be more efficient in promoting photosynthesis than light absorbed by Chl $a$.[‡]   This was the case with phycocyanin in blue-green algae and with both phycocyanin and phycoerythrin in red algae.   The same result was obtained when the fluorescence of Chl $a$ was measured.   Light absorbed directly by Chl $a$ is re-emitted, to some degree, as fluorescent light.   But light energy absorbed by phycobilins and then transferred to Chl $a$ was found to be more efficient in promoting Chl $a$ fluorescence than light absorbed by Chl $a$ itself.   These results were explained on the basis that the algae contain two forms of Chl $a$ in roughly equal amounts: a fluorescent form, active in photosynthesis, and an inactive nonfluorescent form.   Energy absorbed by phycobilins is transferred preferentially to the active form.   Energy absorbed by carotenoids appeared to be transferred preferentially to the inactive form.

Another effect, seemingly related to the foregoing, was the "red drop" phenomenon.   Emerson and Lewis, and later Haxo and Blinks, reported that light absorbed by the "long-wave tail" of the Chl $a$ band, beyond about 680 m$\mu$, is relatively inefficient for photosynthesis in algae.   Figure 3.2 shows this effect in the photosynthesis of a marine alga.   If the light-absorbing pigments were fully and equally effective in promoting photo-

---

[†] See W. Bladergroen, *Problems in Photosynthesis*, Springfield, Ill.: Charles C Thomas, 1960.
[‡] This curious situation had actually been observed by Engelmann in 1884.

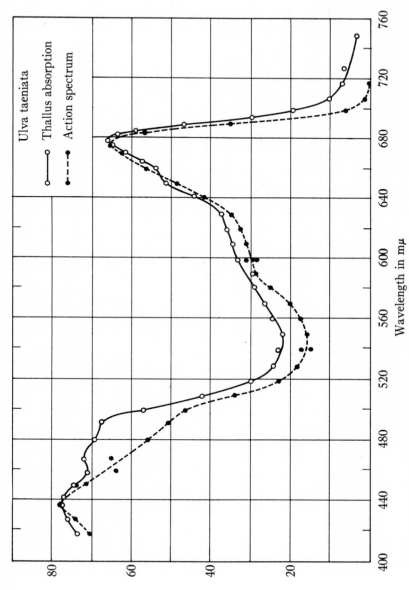

FIGURE 3.2. *Absorption spectrum and action spectrum for photosynthesis in the green alga Ulva, reproduced from a figure by F. Haxo and L. R. Blinks (Reprinted by permissions of the Rockefeller Institute Press and of the authors, from the Journal of General Physiology, March 20, 1950, volume 33, number 4, page 404). Note the relative inefficiency for photosynthesis of light absorbed by Chl a beyond 680 mμ.*

synthesis, the action spectrum† for photosynthesis should coincide with the absorption spectrum. Actually the action spectrum in Figure 3.2 falls dramatically below the absorption spectrum in the far-red part of the Chl *a* band.

These results indicated that something was peculiar about the participation of Chl in photosynthesis. Another peculiarity appeared in the form of "chromatic transients" observed by Blinks and others. If photosynthesis involves only one kind of photochemical act, then all wavelengths of light should have qualitatively the same effect. It should be possible to adjust the intensities of two monochromatic beams of different wavelengths to photosynthetic equivalence. A sudden substitution of one beam for the other should then cause no observable perturbation in the course of photosynthesis. Blinks, measuring $O_2$ evolution in algae, found that this was not the case. In general it was found impossible to adjust the intensities of two beams of different wavelengths so as to eliminate a transient disturbance in the time-course of $O_2$ evolution. But $O_2$ exchange in algae involves respiration and perhaps nonenzymatic photo-oxidations as well as photosynthesis, and so it could not be said conclusively that two distinct photochemical acts are involved in photosynthesis.

The idea that two different photochemical processes can cooperate in the initiation of photosynthesis was given its greatest impetus by some findings of Emerson and collaborators reported in 1956. At this time Emerson had been heavily involved in the controversy with Warburg over quantum efficiency. One of Warburg's claims, in the realm of experimental arts, was that the efficiency of red light (around 650 m$\mu$) for photosynthesis in *Chlorella* could be augmented by mixing in a trace of blue light. No one outside of Warburg's laboratory could corroborate this, but the claim may have helped to provide a starting point for Emerson's discovery of a different kind of "two-light" effect. If so the exhaustive over-extension of the quantum yield controversy was not a complete waste of time.

Emerson showed that the low efficiency of far red ($>680$ m$\mu$) light for photosynthesis in *Chlorella* could be increased by superimposing light of shorter wavelengths. This enhancement phenomenon can be stated in another way. Let $x$ be the rate of photosynthesis produced by a certain intensity of far red light alone, and $y$ that produced by some intensity of shorter wave light. Then if the two beams of light are superimposed, a rate $z$ is observed that is greater than the sum of $x$ and $y$. The degree of enhancement can be expressed as $z/(x + y)$. The enhancement appears

† An action spectrum for a phenomenon is a plot of the magnitude or rate of the phenomenon *vs.* wavelength of the exciting light. It should be measured under such conditions that one can compute the light intensity (in quanta/sec) needed to produce a standard response. The reciprocal of this quantum intensity, plotted against wavelength, can then be compared with an absorption spectrum plotted as "fraction absorbed" *vs.* wavelength.

to result from a more effective utilization of far red light in response to the simultaneous presence of shorter wave light.

The Emerson enhancement phenomenon showed that light of different wavelengths produces qualitatively different effects in promoting photosynthesis. The assumption of "inactive Chl $a$" is insufficient to account for the red-drop effect and is no longer needed to account for the abnormally high efficiency of phycobilins as compared with Chl $a$. A different assumption became necessary and sufficient: that photosynthesis requires the cooperation of two distinct photochemical acts. Light of wavelengths less than about 680 m$\mu$ can effect both acts, but only one is promoted by far red light.

A different kind of experiment, pertinent to these considerations, was performed by G. C. McLeod in French's laboratory. McLeod measured the maximum rate of photosynthesis attainable (that is, the rate under light saturation) in *Chlorella* as a function of wavelength. Beyond 690 m$\mu$ no intensity of light could produce the rates attainable with shorter wavelengths. Again the difference between far red and shorter wave light was shown to be qualitative and not merely quantitative.

With the recognition that photosynthesis involves two different light reactions it was natural to ask what pigments harvest light energy to drive these reactions. This question could be settled through suitable determinations of action spectra. Thus the photosynthetic response to a fixed intensity of 700 m$\mu$ light could be noted, and the enhancement of this response in the presence of shorter wave light measured. By measuring the enhancing effect of the shorter wave light as a function of its wavelength one could identify the pigments that mediate the "short wave reaction." Conversely, with a fixed shorter wavelength and variable far red wavelength, the pigments serving the enhanceable "far red reaction" could be revealed. These techniques have been applied, especially in the laboratories of French (C. S. French, J. Myers, G. C. McLeod, and D. C. Fork) and Rabinowitch (with R. Emerson and Govindjee), to a variety of algae and to chloroplasts. The pattern that has emerged consistently from these measurements is that the far red reaction is mediated by a form of Chl $a$ absorbing maximally at about 683 m$\mu$ (Chl $a$ 680) and the shorter wave reaction is mediated by a variety of pigments, especially phycobilins, Chl $b$, and a form of Chl $a$ absorbing at 673 m$\mu$ (Chl $a$ 670). These results are consistent with the earlier work through which the "red drop" effect was unearthed. Action spectra for Chl $a$ fluorescence indicate that energy absorbed by phycobilins and Chl $b$ is transferred efficiently to the fluorescent Chl $a$ 670 and that Chl $a$ 680 is nonfluorescent. A consistent pattern is lacking for the involvement of carotenoids with one Chl $a$ form or the other; the prevailing impression is that they are associated more closely with Chl $a$ 680. By fractionating *Chlorella* cells, M. B. Allen has shown that Chl $a$ 670 (together with Chl $b$) is bound to one kind of subcellular particle, and Chl $a$ 680 to another. Thus the far red and shorter wave systems are not only functionally distinguishable; they may also be distinct structural entities.

Action spectra for Blinks' chromatic transients in the time course of $O_2$ evolution appear identical to action spectra for the enhancement phenomenon.

Finally, an extremely significant result regarding the interaction of two cooperating light reactions was obtained by Myers and French through a simple experiment. Far red and shorter wave light were administered in the form of alternating flashes, rather than being superimposed. Enhancement could be observed even when the two qualities of light were separated by dark intervals of several seconds. At least one of the two light effects was thus shown to be relatively stable; it could interact with the other several seconds after it had been generated.

In view of the earlier arguments concerning the cooperation of two quanta in a primary photochemical act, the implication of two distinct light reactions in photosynthesis was received with the greatest interest. A major part of research in photosynthesis during the past six years has dealt with a dissection of partial reactions (for example, $O_2$ evolution, formation of reductants, and phosphorylation), with the assignment of such reactions to the far red or the shorter wave effect, and with efforts to coordinate the resulting information in schemes that represent the cooperation of two light reactions.

The conceptions of a photosynthetic unit and a primary photochemical separation of oxidant and reductant have been described as milestones in the elucidation of photosynthesis. The enhancement phenomenon and its implications may be taken as another such milestone: as the starting point of a revolution in the formulations of photosynthesis.

When two cooperating light reactions are visualized, the character of the arguments concerning quantum efficiency and mechanism is at once changed. The argument that 4 quanta per $CO_2$ are not enough, based on an energy budget, remains as valid as before. Nor is there any reason to doubt that 6 to 10 $h\nu/CO_2$ represents the most probable value. But these considerations no longer force a conclusion that photosynthesis begins with a concerted two-quantum reaction. If two different photochemical reactions are of the form

$$h\nu_1 \rightarrow (H)_a + (OH)_a \text{ and } h\nu_2 \rightarrow (H)_b + (OH)_b, \qquad [3.2.1]$$

and if there is some interaction, say between $(OH)_a$ and $(H)_b$, the net production of four reducing and four oxidizing equivalents could be attained in a variety of ways. Then, depending on whether each of the two reactions is a one-quantum or a two-quantum event, any quantum

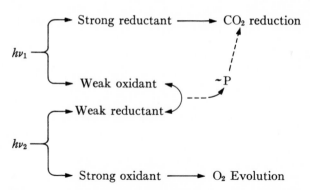

FIGURE 3.3. *A generalized series formulation for the cooperation of two photo-chemical acts in photosynthesis.*

number that is energetically sufficient could be expected. Most current formulations of photosynthesis are of the general form shown in Figure 3.3. One light reaction produces a strong reductant and a weak oxidant; the other yields a weak reductant and a strong oxidant. The strong reductant and oxidant lead to $CO_2$ reduction and $O_2$ evolution respectively; the two weak species may combine in a process that is coupled with phosphorylation. If each light reaction is a one-quantum process in which a single electron is transferred, a total of 8 quanta (four in each reaction) yields 4 equivalents of strong reductant, 4 of strong oxidant, and some energetic phosphate ester (symbolized "$\sim$P"). The same stoichiometry would result if either or both light-reactions were "two-quantum, two-electron-transfer" events. Figure 3.3 is a generalized portrayal of a "series formulation," characterized by a sequential arrangement of the two light reactions. It has two essential properties. First, the combination of weak oxidant and reductant results in eight primary electron transfers yielding four equivalents each of strong oxidant and reductant. Second, the generation of strong reductant (leading to $CO_2$ reduction) is the function of one light reaction, and the production of strong oxidant (the precursor of $O_2$) is the function of the other.

Alternatively, one can construct a "parallel formulation" along the lines of Figure 3.4 (this was recently posed in specific terms by Gaffron). In its purest form each light reaction produces a strong reductant and a strong oxidant. Neither light reaction can promote photosynthesis by itself for reasons of chemistry. For example (as in Gaffron's proposal), the evolution of $O_2$ may require a particular interaction of the two kinds of strong oxidant. When each light reaction has occurred twice, four oxidizing and four reducing equivalents have been formed. If both light reactions were one-quantum events this would correspond to the utiliza-

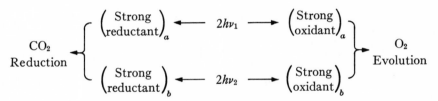

FIGURE 3.4.   *A generalized parallel formulation for the cooperation of two photochemical acts in photosynthesis.*

tion of 4 quanta, an insufficient number according to Franck's energy budget.   Eight quanta per $CO_2$ are required if each light reaction is a two-quantum process that yields one oxidizing and one reducing equivalent.   The interactions of reductants on the one hand and of oxidants on the other, in the course of $CO_2$ reduction and $O_2$ evolution, can be arranged so as to drain a little energy into the formation of high-energy phosphate bonds.

The parallel formulation can of course be generalized further.   For example, a total of eight oxidizing and eight reducing equivalents could be formed at the expense of 8 quanta in one-quantum reactions.   Various patterns of recombination and convergence could then lead eventually to the reduction of one $CO_2$ and the evolution of one $O_2$.   The important characteristic of a parallel formulation is that the functions of $CO_2$ reduction and $O_2$ evolution are shared more or less symmetrically by the two light reactions.

A major alternative to the foregoing conceptions is that one of the two light effects (specifically the one associated with far red light) is an inhibition of photosynthesis and not a reaction essential to photosynthesis. Enhancement is then the expression of an effect of shorter wave light in relieving this inhibition.   This point of view is currently being developed by Franck and will be explored in the next chapter and again in Chapter 13.

We have examined some conceptual implications of the involvement of two light reactions in photosynthesis, and we shall turn next to a delineation of the two reactions on the basis of experimental evidence.

# 4. Current Formulations of Photosynthesis

## 4.1 The Evolution of a Series Formulation

ONCE it had been recognized that photosynthesis involves two light reactions, much of the known light-dependent chemistry of plants could be brought into a new focus. Experiments could be designed and interpreted in terms of the question, "Is this event ($O_2$ evolution, P700 oxidation, et cetera) a property of the far red system, of the shorter wave system, or of both?" An immediate consequence of this activity was that in the period 1960–1961 at least six groups of investigators proposed what was essentially the scheme shown in Figure 3.3: a series formulation in which the shorter wave system (henceforth called System II) forms a strong oxidant leading to $O_2$ evolution, while the far red system (System I) forms a strong reductant that can reduce TPN+ to TPNH. The two systems are connected through a chain of electron carriers. Plastoquinone, Cyt $b$, Cyt $f$, and P700 have been implicated as successive members of this chain. This kind of series formulation is outlined in Figure 4.1. System II raises electrons from a potential of about $+800$ mv (the potential of the oxygen electrode at pH 7) to about zero mv. These electrons "fall" to a lower energy† (about 400 mv potential) through the aforementioned chain of carriers. They are then promoted to a potential around $-400$ mv (sufficient to reduce TPN+) by System I. Phosphorylation can be coupled to the flow of electrons from 0 to $+400$ mv and also to "short circuit" pathways (for example, from $-400$ mv to $+400$ mv) in which TPN+ reduction and $O_2$ evolution are bypassed.

Some of the basic observations leading to this series formulation will now be listed.

---

† The reducing potential of an electron is a direct expression of its energy. Thus a change from 0 to $+400$ mv represents a loss in energy of 0.4 electron volts, or 9 kcal/mole.

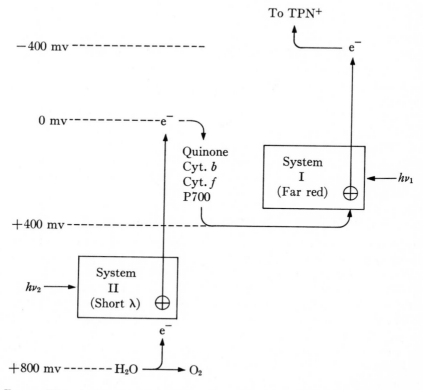

FIGURE 4.1.    *A current representation of the series formulation.    Detailed explanation in the text.*

1. (R. Hill and F. Bendall *et al.*) Cytochromes *f* and *b* are found in plants and engage in light-induced reactions. In pale yellow-green leaves it can be seen that light causes oxidation of Cyt *f* and reduction of Cyt *b*. The oxidation potentials of Cyt *f* and Cyt *b* are about +360 and 0 mv, respectively.

2. (L. N. M. Duysens, J. Amesz, and B. M. Kamp) In the alga *Porphyridium*, Cyt *f* is oxidized by far red light. If shorter wave light is then superimposed the Cyt *f* becomes reduced. The herbicide DCMU, which inhibits evolution of $O_2$, also inhibits the cytochrome-reducing action of shorter wave light. DCMU does not inhibit the cytochrome-oxidizing action of far red light, nor (citing N. I. Bishop and also Vernon and Zaugg) does it inhibit the photoreduction of $CO_2$ or $TPN^+$ in cases where the $O_2$-evolving mechanism has been replaced by an artificial electron donor. Thus the shorter wave System II is associated with $O_2$ evolution, reduction

of Cyt $f$, and sensitivity to DCMU. The far red System I promotes reduction of $TPN^+$ (and $CO_2$) and oxidation of Cyt $f$, and is insensitive to DCMU. In the presence of DCMU the action spectra for Cyt $f$ oxidation and $TPN^+$ reduction both show the Chl $a_{680}$ peak characteristic of System I. Recently Duysens has shown that plastoquinone, as well as Cyt $f$, is reduced by shorter wave light and oxidized by far red light. The criterion for reduction of plastoquinone is a bleaching centered at 255 m$\mu$.

3. (B. Kok and G. Hoch) In algae and chloroplasts P700 is oxidized by far red light and reduced by shorter wave light in complete analogy to the behavior of Cyt $f$ as described by Duysens $et\ al.$† The oxidation potential of P700 is about $+470$ mv. Ferricyanide can oxidize P700 and thereby can replace or bypass the oxidizing action of far red light. Various reductants, by reducing P700, can replace the reducing action of shorter wave light. The reduction of oxidized P700 by System II is blocked by DCMU. In view of the identification of P700 as a specialized form of Chl $a$ (see Section 2.3) it might be more realistic to regard this substance as a central agent in System I rather than as an accessory electron carrier.

4. (M. Losada, F. R. Whatley, and D. I. Arnon) Evolution of $O_2$ and reduction of $TPN^+$ by chloroplasts can be demonstrated separately through the use of redox agents in the range 0 to $+400$ mv. The separate processes show different action spectra, $O_2$ evolution being promoted by Chl $b$ (that is, by System II).

5. (H. Kautsky, W. Appell, and H. Amann) Transients in the intensity of fluorescence in $Chlorella$, and the effects of inhibitors on these transients, are explained simply in terms of a series formulation, the fluorescence being emitted by the Chl $a$ of System II.

6. (H. T. Witt $et\ al.$) Some light-induced absorbancy changes, associated indirectly with reduction of plastoquinone, are mediated by the pigments (Chl $b$ and Chl $a_{670}$) of System II. The reversal of these changes in the dark is accelerated by oxidants of potential greater than 0 mv. The changes corresponding to oxidation of P700 and Cyt $f$ are mediated by the Chl $a_{680}$ of System I, and by P700 itself. The return of oxidized P700 and Cyt $f$ to their reduced forms is accelerated by reductants of potential less than $+400$ mv. As noted in Chapter 2 the kinetics of the light-induced oxidations of P700 and Cyt $f$ indicate that the former precedes the latter.

The detailed spectrophotometric observations of Witt and collaborators continue to grow; some of the light-induced absorbancy changes observed in spinach chloroplasts are listed in Table 4.1. The changes of Types 2a and 2′, representing oxidation of Cyt and P700 by System I, have already been discussed. The light-induced change denoted Type 2b is missing in

† The light reactions of P700 and Cyt $f$ described in Chapter 2, Section 2.3 are those induced by far red light.

TABLE 4.1. Light-induced absorbancy changes in chloroplasts as described by H. T. Witt and collaborators. The Type 0 change is seen only in denatured material.

| Type | Δ O. D. (+ or − and wavelength in mμ) | Occurrence at −150°C | Provisional identification |
|------|------|------|------|
| 0 | −430, +450–600 | | Chl $a$ in excited triplet state |
| 1 | −430, +520 | reversible | Chl $a$ in a metastable (reduced?) state |
| 2a | −420 | irreversible | oxidized cytochrome |
| 2b | −475, +515 | absent | associated with quinone reduction |
| 2′ | −430, −705 | irreversible | oxidized P700 |
| — | −255 | | reduced plastoquinone |

chloroplasts that have been extracted with petroleum ether; it can be restored by evaporating the extract back onto the chloroplasts. V. Lynch and French had already shown that Hill reaction activity could be abolished and restored in this way, and Bishop had shown that the extractable factor necessary for the Hill reaction is plastoquinone. Witt *et al.* therefore associate the Type 2b reaction with quinone reduction in System II. The decay of the Type 2b reaction in darkness is accelerated by oxidizing substances. Reduction of plastoquinone may be manifested more directly by the light-induced bleaching at 255 mμ, but Witt *et al.* associate this change with both the far red and the shorter wave systems on the basis of its kinetics. Nevertheless the major part of the absorption change at 255 mμ shows the same kinetics as the change of Type 2b. The change listed as Type I occurs reversibly at low temperature; it is inhibited by heat-denaturation or detergent treatment. When inhibited, it is replaced by a change that suggests formation of the Chl $a$ triplet excited state. The Type I change is inhibited also by paramagnetic substances such as $O_2$ or NO. It is therefore described as a metastable state of Chl $a$ formed *via* the triplet excited state.† Any relationship of the changes of Types 0 and 1 to photosynthesis remains uncertain.

The work of Duysens *et al.* on light-induced oxidation and reduction of Cyt $f$ in *Porphyridium* has been extended by J. M. Olson, J. A. Bergeron, and R. M. Smillie with the algae *Anacystis* and *Euglena*. Olson *et al.* have shown that far red light is ten to forty times as effective as shorter wave light in promoting oxidation of cytochromes in these algae. The

† Paramagnetic substances encourage both the formation and the quenching of triplet excited states of molecules; see Part II.

response to shorter wave light is diphasic, showing an initial oxidation of Cyt followed by a partial re-reduction under continuous illumination. In *Euglena* the predominant light-reacting Cyt is a *c* type, rather than Cyt *f*. This Cyt *c* can be extracted from *Euglena*; the extracted preparation then shows a light-induced reduction of a *b*-type Cyt. These observations are consistent with a formulation in which the cytochromes form a link between Systems I and II, being oxidized by the former and reduced by the latter.

Further support for the formulation of Figure 4.1 comes from the recent work of Bishop and Gaffron on hydrogen-adaptation and mutations in the alga *Scenedesmus*. As noted earlier, Gaffron had discovered that this alga can be trained, through incubation with $H_2$, to perform a "bacterial" photosynthesis in which $H_2$ serves as electron donor for the reduction of $CO_2$. In terms of Figure 4.1 the $H_2$-adapted algae are employing System I only, using electrons from $H_2$ instead of electrons from System II. A determining factor in this choice of electron donor appears to be the activity of the enzyme hydrogenase. Under strong illumination the adapted algae lose their state of adaptation and revert to "normal" photosynthesis. Bishop has shown that far red light (705 m$\mu$) is more effective than shorter wave light in promoting the photoreduction of $CO_2$ at the expense of $H_2$. At the same time far red light is relatively unable to cause reversion from photoreduction to complete photosynthesis. The reversion effect is blocked entirely by DCMU; unusually high rates of photoreduction can then be attained at light intensities that would cause reversion in the absence of DCMU. With DCMU present far red light is much more effective for photoreduction than is shorter wave light. Bishop has also isolated mutants of *Scenedesmus* in which either System I or System II does not function. Mutants of the first kind exhibit a Hill reaction but cannot reduce $TPN^+$ or $CO_2$ photosynthetically. Those of the second kind behave like DCMU-poisoned cells, showing photoreduction with $H_2$ as substrate but lacking the $O_2$-evolving mechanism. Somewhat similar mutants of the alga *Chlamydomonas* have been obtained by R. P. Levine.

Measurements of electron spin resonance, notably by B. Commoner, M. Calvin, M. B. Allen, H. Beinert, B. Kok, L. P. Vernon, R. P. Levine, and their collaborators, have yielded a coherent pattern of observations consistent with a series formulation. Two kinds of light-induced ESR signal can be observed in green plants and algae. Signal 1 has a relatively narrow band and no fine structure; it decays in a matter of seconds in the dark. Signal 2 is broader, displays secondary structure, and usually requires minutes or hours to disappear after illumination has ceased. Signal 1, which occurs irreversibly at 77°K, shows a close correlation with the oxidation of P700. It may indeed be a manifestation of oxidized

P700. Signal 2 behaves as if it belongs to an organic radical that is formed during the operation of the $O_2$-evolving mechanism. As the foregoing implies, Signal 1 is associated with far red excitation and Signal 2 with shorter wave excitation.

It can be seen from Figure 4.1 that two kinds of Hill reaction might occur. In one kind, $O_2$ evolution is coupled with reduction of an electron acceptor through System II alone. The Hill oxidant (or electron acceptor) replaces System I in this case. Alternatively, the acceptor could replace $TPN^+$ in receiving electrons delivered by System I. The Hill reaction would then involve both Systems I and II in coupling evolution of $O_2$ with reduction of the acceptor. In the latter case, but not in the former, the enhancement effect should be associated with the Hill reaction as well as with complete photosynthesis. At present there are conflicting reports on this matter; electron acceptors such as ferricyanide can probably invade the photosynthetic pathways at two points: between Systems I and II and also on the high energy side of System I.

The manner in which these pathways are coupled to phosphorylation has been the subject of an enormous amount of study in recent years. No attempt will be made to deal with this intricate subject; instead the reader is referred to the publications of D. I. Arnon, A. T. Jagendorf, B. Vennesland, and others.

The foregoing evidence for the series formulation of Figure 4.1 must be regarded as impressive, but not sufficient to exclude other formulations. The alternatives range from completely different schemes down to slight variations on the "series" theme. As an example of the latter, W. D. McElroy and H. H. Seliger have suggested that Cyt $f$ is the only electron carrier connecting System II with the P700 of System I. Other carriers such as quinone and Cyt $b$ are placed in a cyclic pathway leading from the "top" of System I ($-400$ mv) back to Cyt $f$. The scheme of Figure 4.1 can be regarded as representing a class of series formulations, all of which have certain characteristic properties. Light absorbed by System I generates a strong reductant (capable of reducing $TPN^+$) and a weak oxidant such as oxidized Cyt $f$. System II produces a strong oxidant (a precursor of $O_2$) and a weak reductant. The weak reductant of System II interacts with the weak oxidant of System I. The light-harvesting pigments of the two systems are such that light of wavelength less than 680 m$\mu$ can serve both systems, but far red light can serve System I only.

The "cooperation of two quanta" comes, in a series formulation, from the fact that two different light-driven electron transfer acts are needed to produce one equivalent of strong reductant ($\sim-400$ mv) and one of strong oxidant ($\sim+800$ mv). For the purpose of interpreting the quantum requirement of photosynthesis, this sort of cooperation removes the necessity of visualizing a concerted two-quantum primary photochemical act.†

The position of bacterial photosynthesis (and of photoreduction in $H_2$-adapted algae) is simple and natural in terms of a series formulation. The photosynthetic bacteria use a counterpart of System I, with a cytochrome of the $c$ type in place of Cyt $f$ and P870 in place of P700. Since they lack System II, the bacteria cannot evolve $O_2$ and must rely on oxidizable substrates to provide electrons for the operation of their "System I." The fact that no one has been able to observe enhancement in bacterial photosynthesis supports the idea that the bacteria use only one kind of photochemical system. If two different light reactions are to be invoked in the bacteria, it must be assumed either that both reactions are served by one light-harvesting system or that the failure to observe enhancement is due to trivial technical difficulties.

## 4.2 Alternatives to the Series Formulation

From the time of its enunciation the series formulation as represented in Figure 4.1 has been criticized for a variety of reasons. One basis of criticism has been the remarkable constancy of the quantum efficiency of photosynthesis throughout most of the visible spectrum. Emerson and Lewis showed, for example, that except for a decline in the region of carotenoid absorption the efficiency of photosynthesis in *Chlorella* under monochromatic light varies no more than $\pm 10\%$ from 400 to 680 m$\mu$. A series formulation (Figure 3.3 or 4.1) predicts that the two light reactions must be in balanced operation for efficient photosynthesis. For every light-driven electron transfer in System II, one is required in System I to complete the photochemical sequence. If the pigments of System II should absorb energy twice as fast as the pigments of System I, half the energy absorbed by System II ought to be wasted. An imbalance might also have more serious consequences such as a local depletion or accumulation of $H^+$ ions. It cannot be believed that the light-harvesting pigments of Systems I and II are so perfectly matched, from 400 to 680 m$\mu$, that the two systems absorb light equally at every wavelength. Thus in blue-green algae at 630 m$\mu$ the absorption by phycocyanin (serving System II) should far exceed the absorption by a "far red" form of Chl $a$. In terms of Figure 4.1, most of the phycocyanin-absorbed light should be wasted in steady-state photosynthesis. To circumvent this difficulty and retain a series formulation it is necessary to invent some sort of special assumption.

† Although the need for a concerted two-quantum reaction has been removed in a series formulation, it does not follow that the possibility of such a reaction has been eliminated. It remains possible, for example, that in System II a pair of electrons is transferred from water to an electron acceptor in a photochemical sequence that utilizes two quanta.

Thus one might say that energy can be transferred from the pigments of System II to those of System I, but not in the opposite direction. So far, so good: the assumption is natural because the long wave Chl $a$ could act as an "energy sink" for excitation produced in the shorter wave pigments. But now a switching device must be introduced, such that energy is transferred from System II to System I only as needed (that is, only when System I is "under-driven"). Actually this special assumption is not as forced as it first seems. Consider that P700 is the "reaction center Chl" of System I. Then suppose that P700 (but not Chl $a_{680}$) is in a position to accept excitation energy from the pigments of System II. As long as System I can keep pace with System II, the P700 can be maintained in its bleached (oxidized) form and energy transfer will not occur. But as soon as System I falls behind System II, the reduced (unbleached) form of P700 tends to predominate. Energy can then be transferred to P700; some of the energy absorbed by System II is thus channeled automatically to System I as needed. We shall see later that there is reason to place the Chl $a$ of System I in an environment of protein and lipid, protected from water, and the pigments of System II in an aqueous environment, with the reaction center of System I (that is, P700) extending into the aqueous environment. This is just the kind of structural arrangement that would allow a selective transfer of excitation energy from the "System II" pigments to P700 but not to the light-harvesting Chl $a$ of System I.

The foregoing switching mechanism is not the only one that can be visualized. A photochemical reaction center, served by an ensemble of light-harvesting molecules, should act as a trap for excitation energy when it is not actually engaged in photochemistry. As soon as the reaction center itself becomes excited, it probably loses the property of an energy sink until it has returned to its "resting" condition. On this basis one could speculate that energy absorbed in System II is used first at the hypothetical reaction center of System II, but if that reaction center is involved in photochemistry some energy will "spill over" to the light-harvesting pigment of System I. The spilling over will be greater when the reaction center of System II is saturated (that is, when System II is being over-driven). Although this mechanism would tend to balance the two light reactions, a switch based on the selective transfer of energy to P700 should be able to give a more precise balance.

The problem of balancing the two light reactions can thus be settled, but at the cost of additional assumptions that make the series formulation more complicated. With these assumptions we have arrived at a picture that was dictated in the first place by the enhancement phenomenon: one photochemical system (the shorter wave System II) can bring about complete photosynthesis; the other (System I) can drive only a part of the photosynthetic mechanism.

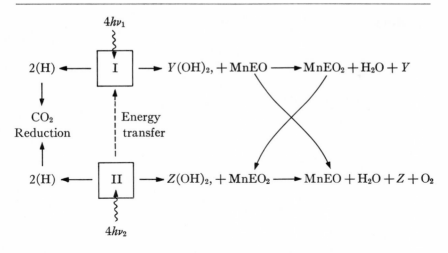

FIGURE 4.2. *A parallel formulation as suggested by Gaffron.*

Another line of evidence against the series formulation, pursued especially by Gaffron, has to do with the position of bacterial photosynthesis. If the bacteria carry on photosynthesis by means of a counterpart of System I it follows that the green plants and algae possess an entire photochemical system (System II) that the bacteria lack. The most logical evolutionary picture is that a bacterial type of photosynthesis preceded that of the green plants and algae. In many ways the purple bacteria are more primitive (that is, more unspecialized) than most algae. We are led to suppose, then, that the green plants and algae evolved an entire photochemical system capable of liberating $O_2$ from water. This second system would probably have been nonfunctional until all of its elements (pigments, reaction center, $O_2$-evolving enzymes, et cetera) had been developed. Such a complicated evolutionary maneuver seems most unlikely if it had no value until it had been completed. Gaffron preferred to argue that the difference between green plant and bacterial photosynthesis is minimal: it is essentially the presence or absence of a single enzyme needed for the terminal stage of $O_2$ evolution. Manganese was implicated in this crucial enzyme on the basis of some effects of Mn deficiency in plants. Gaffron, following this line of thought, has proposed a parallel formulation as outlined in Figure 4.2.† In this scheme Systems I and II engage in photochemical acts that are nearly identical: each system mediates a succession of two-quantum events in which water is split and strong reductants and oxidants are formed. The oxidants, denoted $Y(OH)_2$ and $Z(OH)_2$, inter-

† Figure 4.2 is not identical to the version published by Gaffron; inconsequential modifications were introduced to facilitate the ensuing discussion.

act through a manganese-containing enzyme (written MnEO in its reduced form and $MnEO_2$ in its oxidized form) in such a way that $O_2$ is evolved. Through this interaction the oxidants are restored to their reduced forms, $Y$ and $Z$. Energy transfer from System II to System I is allowed in order to account for the red-drop and enhancement phenomena. By appropriate insertions of Cyt $f$ and other substances in the reaction pathways one could account for the various observations that led to the series formulation.

The formulation of Figure 4.2 was not intended to be a specific and complete description of photosynthesis; it was offered as a way of thinking alternative to the series formulation. In this model Gaffron has kept the differences between Systems I and II minimal and has emphasized the similarity of bacterial and green plant photosynthesis. In the bacteria, Systems I and II might be indistinguishable. The absence of an enhancement effect in bacterial photosynthesis indicates that if the two systems are not identical they are at least served by the same kinds of light-harvesting pigments. The bacteria, lacking MnEO, must use electron-donor substrates to restore $Y(OH)_2$ and $Z(OH)_2$ to the reduced forms $Y$ and $Z$ (again, $Y$ and $Z$ might be identical in the photosynthetic bacteria).

Gaffron's parallel formulation makes the evolution of photosynthetic organisms more feasible and preserves a strict biochemical unity of the bacterial and green plant photosyntheses. Probably the best evidence in favor of this point of view is found in the quantum requirement for bacterial photosynthesis. According to the series formulation, photosynthetic bacteria use electron-donor substrates in place of System II. They should therefore need only 4 quanta to reduce one $CO_2$ molecule, in contrast to the 8 quanta needed by green plants and algae. In a parallel formulation like that of Figure 4.2 the quantum requirements for the bacterial and green plant photosyntheses should be equal. H. Larsen and van Niel, measuring the quantum efficiency of bacterial photosynthesis, found a requirement of about 10 quanta per $CO_2$. This value appeared to be independent of the redox potential of the substrate; it supports a parallel formulation through the foregoing argument. But as is usually the case there are ways to undermine the force of the argument. Consider that the evidence implicating UQ as a reaction partner of P870 is quite clear, whereas that linking P700 oxidation with PQ reduction is tenuous. Imagine then that (1) the reductant formed in the "System I" reaction has a potential of $-400$ mv, capable of reducing $TPN^+$, and (2) the reductant formed in the bacterial system, reduced UQ, has a potential *in vivo* equal to the measured *in vitro* potential of 0 mv. The difference of 400 mv per electron could account for the relative inefficiency of bacterial photosynthesis. In this view the bacteria, unable to make a strong reductant directly, can only generate high energy phosphate bonds through a cycle of electron flow from reduced UQ to oxidized Cyt.  They must then resort to reductive dephosphorylation in order to generate such things as reduced pyridine nucleotide.  As was mentioned in Section 1.2 this is an extreme point of view, but it is not untenable.

Recent measurements of chromatic transients in $O_2$ evolution, conducted by French and Fork, tend to favor a parallel formulation or perhaps a mixed series-parallel network.  Evolution and consumption of $O_2$ appears to involve both Systems I and II in a complicated way.

One could undoubtedly concoct a theory embracing both the series and the parallel formulations.  With enough complexity all of the foregoing data and arguments could be accommodated.  The result would surely be a useless exercise in network construction: a demonstration of the fact that a sufficiently complicated model can explain everything.

Regardless of these problems of interaction, the existence of two photochemical systems poses new questions about the identification of photosynthetic units and the interpretation of Emerson and Arnold's original flashing light experiments.  Does the 300-molecule unit pertain to System I, or II, or both?  The emergence of these questions was paralleled by new evidence about the photosynthetic unit, and the situation seems to remain straightforward.  The fact that the ratio of P700 or Cyt $f$ to Chl $a$ is about 1:300 indicates that System I entails a unit of 300 Chl $a$ molecules.  For System II there is the evidence based on inhibition of the Hill reaction: one molecule of DCMU for every 200 Chl molecules causes complete inhibition, and fragmentation of chloroplasts leads to a marked inhibition of $O_2$ evolution when the particles contain fewer than about 200 Chl molecules apiece.

The clearest evidence for photochemical reaction centers pertains to System I and to the bacterial chromatophore.  For these systems the evidence lies in the physical and photochemical properties of P700, P870, and cytochromes.  With regard to System II in green plants and algae there is little or no concrete evidence for a reaction center or for a photochemical reaction of Chl.  The "Type 1" reaction of Witt (see Table 4.1) has been interpreted as reflecting the conversion of Chl to a metastable or a reduced state.  The magnitude of the change corresponds to the alteration of one Chl molecule in 300.  But there is no basis for associating this change with System II, or even with the photochemistry of photosynthesis.

These considerations lead us to the final possibility that there is only one photochemical reaction center for photosynthesis in green plants and algae. One way of formulating this possibility is to start with a series formulation and to eliminate the chain of electron carriers between Systems I and II, allowing the reaction centers of these systems to merge into one "master" reaction center.  Very recently Kok has suggested that P700 serves as

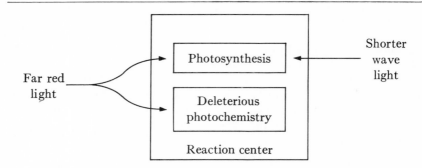

FIGURE 4.3.   *A possible basis for the low efficiency of far red light in photosynthesis,
according to Franck.*

"reaction center Chl" for both Systems I and II.   In its reduced form the
pigment absorbs at 705 m$\mu$ and acts as an energy sink for far red (System
I) excitation.   Photochemical oxidation of P700 converts it to a substance
absorbing at 690 m$\mu$.   In this form, as "P690," it acts as an energy sink
for System II.   At present it would be premature to assess this possibility
critically.

A completely different approach has been followed recently by Franck
and collaborators.   In the series and parallel formulations already
described, far red light has been assumed to promote only a part of the
photochemistry of photosynthesis.   This has been the basis for understanding the red-drop and enhancement phenomena.   Franck suggests
that these phenomena may be caused in part by parasitic or destructive
photochemical events.   Far red excitation tends to promote these deleterious reactions, and shorter wave light blocks the utilization of far red
light.   This state of affairs is sketched in Figure 4.3.   A single photochemical reaction center receives excitation energy from the entire ensemble of pigments (accessory pigments and all the forms of Chl).   Far red
light and shorter wave light are equally capable of promoting the entire
photochemistry of photosynthesis.   But far red light can also promote
deleterious photo-oxidations.   While the reaction center is engaged in
photochemistry it will not accept additional excitation energy from its
surroundings.   The deleterious reactions will therefore be suppressed if the
proportion of shorter wave light to far red light is kept high.   Stated
differently, by flooding the reaction center with shorter wave light one
can block the entry of far red light.   The red-drop and enhancement
effects can thus be explained without the necessity of assuming that
photosynthesis itself involves two different photochemical reactions.

Much of the evidence leading to a series formulation can be explained on the basis of Franck's model. Thus the oxidations of P700 and Cyt $f$ by far red light can be associated in part with the deleterious photochemistry. In the absence of $O_2$ the deleterious reactions are suppressed, and the full capability of far red light in promoting photosynthesis can be seen. By following this train of thought one can accommodate the results pertaining to hydrogen-adapted algae, and to the effects of DCMU.

The special ability of far red light to promote parasitic photochemical events can be put on a rational physical basis; we shall return to this point in Part III. Another physical argument, based on the intensity of fluorescence in algae, has caused Franck to insist that the photochemistry of photosynthesis involves two distinct light-reactions even though this duality is not needed to explain the enhancement effect. The two reactions involve a single "reaction center Chl" in an obligatorily alternating sequence of photochemical acts. A detailed description of this model will be offered after its physical basis has been developed.

## 4.3 A Concluding Evaluation

At this writing the series formulation enjoys the greatest popularity as an explanation for enhancement and as a model for the photochemical part of photosynthesis. This popular acceptance derives from the simplicity of the formulation, from the straightforward way in which it explains the variety of observations listed in Section 4.1, and from the appealingly clear position that can be assigned to bacterial photosynthesis. The critics of a series formulation have not taken the trouble to show thoroughly how the observations of Duysens, Witt, Kok, et cetera, could be accommodated plausibly by other schemes. Even Gaffron, the most outspoken recent critic of the series formulation, has now become co-author (with Bishop) of a series formulation accounting for the behavior of $H_2$-adapted algae. Bishop and Gaffron did not comment on the relationship of bacterial photosynthesis to their series formulation.

We have seen that the most concrete evidence relating to photochemical reaction centers involves the light-induced oxidation of P700 in green plants and algae and of P870 or P890 in photosynthetic bacteria. The parallelism of these events is in pleasing agreement with the correspondence between System I (of green plants) and the bacterial system, as implied by the series formulation. Both pigments (P700 and P870) appear to be specialized chlorophylls. The light-induced oxidation of each is attended by an ESR signal. Each pigment is linked in some way to an oxidizable cytochrome. But we have also seen the disquieting possibility that the light reactions of P700 and P870 may bear only a secondary relationship to photosynthesis. Franck contends that the bleaching of P700 is mainly a sign of parasitic photo-oxidations. In purple bacteria the oxidation of Cyt proceeds in dim light, whereas the bleaching of P870 occurs only if the Cyt is kept oxidized. We should certainly not abandon the idea that P700 and P870 are important reagents in the photochemistry of photosynthesis, but we would do well to maintain a flexible attitude toward the role of these pigments and also toward the validity of the series formulation.

II

# Descriptive Molecular Physics

# 5. Introduction:
# The Biophysical Problems of Photosynthesis

THE CONCEPTION of photosynthetic units and photochemical reaction centers has provided a statement of the physical problems of photosynthesis. Light quanta are absorbed by Chl and accessory pigments. The excitation energy migrates in an ensemble of pigment molecules and is collected efficiently at the sites of photochemistry. At these sites the energy promotes the photochemical events that initiate the chemistry of photosynthesis. The mechanisms of these processes (absorption, transfer, and primary utilization of light energy) are the subject of the biophysical problems.

To deal with these problems we must understand the nature of excited states in Chl and other substances, and the behavior of such excited molecules when they interact with one another. A descriptive review of some aspects of molecular physics will therefore be appropriate. We shall begin by considering the states of electrons in atoms and proceed to the states that are generated when atoms interact in molecules. A description of molecular excited states will be followed by an examination of the optical and photochemical properties of chlorophylls in dilute solution. Some consequences of molecular interactions will then be explored; a consideration of energy migration and charge transfer in molecular aggregates will bring our survey of molecular physics to a close. We shall then be in a position to discuss the physical behavior of photosynthetic pigments and reaction center constituents in their natural state.

# 6. States of Electrons in Atoms

## 6.1 Quantization, Russell-Saunders Coupling, and the Pauli Exclusion Principle

THE STATES of electrons in atoms are governed by two principles: the quantization of physical parameters and the Pauli exclusion principle. An electron bound to an atom may not have an arbitrary energy, spatial distribution, momentum, et cetera. These physical parameters are restricted, according to the principle of quantization, to a discrete set of values. The discrete values define quantum states of an atomic electron; thus a detailed state is specified by giving the (quantized) values of several independent parameters relating to the energy and angular motion of the electron. The Pauli principle imposes the further restriction that no two electrons in an atom can be in the same detailed state. This corresponds to the classical postulate that two things cannot be in the same place at the same time.

Four parameters suffice to specify the state of an atomic electron. The first of these is the total energy, given approximately by the expression†

$$E = -\frac{2\pi^2 m Z^2 e^4}{n^2 h^2},$$ [6.1.1]

where $m$ and $e$ are the mass and charge of the electron, $Z$ is the atomic number, $h$ is Planck's constant, and $n$ takes on the integral values 1, 2, 3, . . . . The *total quantum number* $n$ thus specifies roughly‡ the total energy of the electron. The value $n = 1$ corresponds to the first "shell" of electrons in an atom (the $K$ shell), and so forth.

The second parameter, specified by the *azimuthal quantum number* $\ell$, is the angular momentum associated (in classical language) with orbital motion of the electron. The value of orbital angular momentum is $(h/2\pi)\sqrt{\ell(\ell+1)}$. The corresponding magnetic moment is

$$(e/2mc)(h/2\pi)\sqrt{\ell(\ell+1)}.$$

---

† The energy is formally negative because the potential energy is taken arbitrarily to be zero in the completely ionized condition.

‡ The energy as given by Equation [6.1.1] is modified by electrostatic and magnetic interactions among the electrons.

For an electron having a particular value of $n$, the possible values of $\ell$ are zero and all positive integers up to $n - 1$. Thus a "$K$ shell electron" ($n = 1$) can have only the value $\ell = 0$; an electron in the $L$ shell ($n = 2$) can have $\ell = 0$ or 1, et cetera. An electron with $\ell = 0$ is called an $s$ electron; electrons with $\ell = 1, 2, 3, \ldots$ are called $p$, $d$, $f$, $g$, $h$, and so forth.

An electron that has some angular momentum (that is, $\ell > 0$) can be imagined to occupy an orbit having a particular orientation. The associated magnetic moment then has a certain direction, specified by the *magnetic quantum number* $m_\ell$. To give meaning to such an orientation a frame of reference must be provided in the form of an external magnetic field. The number $m_\ell$ then expresses the direction of the orbital magnetic moment relative to the direction of the external field. Quantization of $m_\ell$ implies that the strength of interaction between the two magnetic fields (the field of the orbiting electron and the external field) can take on only a discrete set of values. In another sense this quantization expresses the number of independent orientations that an orbit could have in three-dimensional space, as governed by the symmetry properties of that orbit. The physical quantity expressed by $m_\ell$ is the projection of the orbital angular momentum vector along the axis of the external field. This projected component has the value $(h/2\pi)m_\ell$ where the allowed values of $m_\ell$ are $0, \pm 1, \pm 2, \cdots, \pm \ell$. The relationships between the quantum numbers $\ell$ and $m_\ell$ are shown in Figure 6.1 for the case $\ell = 2$; $m_\ell = 0, \pm 1, \pm 2$.

The remaining parameter is the orientation of the angular momentum (and magnetic moment) associated classically with the spin of an electron about its own axis. The magnitude of this effect is fixed, amounting to $(h/2\pi)\sqrt{s(s + 1)}$, where the spin quantum number $s$ has the fixed value $\frac{1}{2}$. The spin angular momentum is therefore $(h/2\pi)(\sqrt{3}/2)$. The corresponding magnetic moment is $(e/mc)(h/2\pi)(\sqrt{3}/2)$. The orientation of the spin can have either of two values (roughly parallel or anti-parallel) relative to an external field. These orientations are specified by a *spin magnetic quantum number* $m_s$, which can be $+\frac{1}{2}$ or $-\frac{1}{2}$. Thus if two electrons in an atom have the same values for the quantum numbers $n, \ell$, and $m_\ell$ they can differ by having opposite values of $m_s$.

Just as the interaction between an electron and an external field is quantized in a way that is represented by $m_\ell$ and $m_s$, so are the mutual interactions among the electrons in an atom governed by quantization rules. For the lighter atoms a good approximation is given by the rules of Russell-Saunders (or R-S) coupling. In this manner of coupling the orbital angular momenta of the several electrons are combined (in accordance with a rule to be described) to give a resultant total orbital angular momentum for the atom. The individual spins are combined likewise to give a resultant total spin. The total spin and orbital momenta are then combined

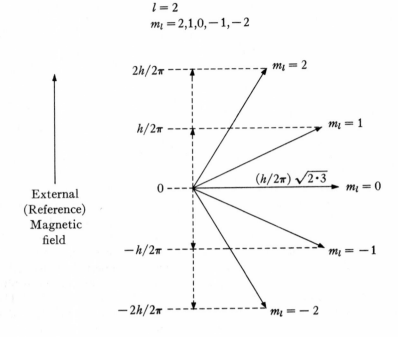

$$l = 2$$
$$m_l = 2, 1, 0, -1, -2$$

Orbital angular momentum $= (h/2\pi)\sqrt{l(l+1)}$

Axial component of orbital angular momentum $= m_l(h/2\pi)$

FIGURE 6.1. *Quantization of the axial component of orbital angular momentum of an atomic electron. The projection along the axis of an external magnetic field must be a multiple of* $h/2\pi$.

to yield a resultant total angular momentum. The rules are as follows. The total orbital angular momentum, specified by the quantum number $L$, is the resultant of a vector addition of the individual momenta specified by values of $\ell$. The resultant must have a magnitude $(h/2\pi)\sqrt{L(L+1)}$, where $L$ is an integer or zero. The possible ways of performing this addition are illustrated in Figure 6.2 for the case of two electrons with $\ell = 1$ and $\ell = 2$, respectively. Note that in this case $L$ can be 1, 2, or 3. Individual spin vectors are added similarly, with the further restriction that the total spin quantum number $S$ is an integer or zero when the number of electrons is even and a half-integer when the number is odd: the total spin angular momentum is $(h/2\pi)\sqrt{S(S+1)}$ with $S = 0, 1, 2, \ldots$ (even number of electrons) or $\frac{1}{2}, \frac{3}{2}, \ldots$ (odd number of electrons).

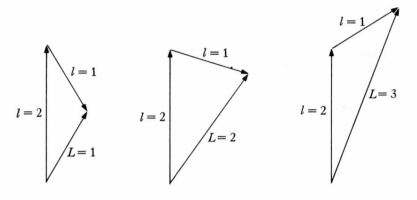

Magnitudes of vectors:

$(h/2\pi)\sqrt{2}$ for $l$ or $L = 1$
$(h/2\pi)\sqrt{6}$ for $l$ or $L = 2$
$(h/2\pi)\sqrt{12}$ for $L = 3$

FIGURE 6.2.   *Vector addition of the angular momenta of two atomic electrons, obeying the rule that the magnitude must be* $(h/2\pi)\sqrt{L(L+1)}$ *for the vector sum.*

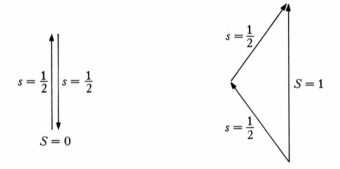

Magnitudes of vectors:

$(h/2\pi)\sqrt{\dfrac{1}{2}\cdot\dfrac{3}{2}}$ for $s = \dfrac{1}{2}$

$(h/2\pi)\sqrt{1\cdot 2}$ for $S = 1$

FIGURE 6.3.   *Addition of antiparallel and "parallel" electron spin vectors.*

TABLE 6.1. Distribution of electrons in atomic shells according to the quantum states allowed by the Pauli principle. The quantum numbers are explained in the text.

| Atomic shell | $n$ | $\ell$ | $m_\ell$ | $m_s$ | Number of electrons | Designation |
|---|---|---|---|---|---|---|
| K | 1 | 0 | 0 | $\frac{1}{2}, -\frac{1}{2}$ | 2 | $1s$ |
| L | 2 | 0 | 0 | $\frac{1}{2}, -\frac{1}{2}$ | 2 | $2s$ |
| | | 1 | 1, 0, −1 | $\frac{1}{2}, -\frac{1}{2}$ | 6 | $2p$ |
| M | 3 | 0 | 0 | $\frac{1}{2}, -\frac{1}{2}$ | 2 | $3s$ |
| | | 1 | 1, 0, −1 | $\frac{1}{2}, -\frac{1}{2}$ | 6 | $3p$ |
| | | 2 | 2, 1, 0, −1, −2 | $\frac{1}{2}, -\frac{1}{2}$ | 10 | $3d$ |

Recall that for each electron the spin angular momentum is

$$(h/2\pi)\ \sqrt{\tfrac{1}{2}(\tfrac{1}{2}+1)}.$$

The allowed vector additions then give $S = 0$ or $1$ for the combination of two electrons, $S = \frac{1}{2}$ or $\frac{3}{2}$ for three electrons, $S = 0$, $1$, or $2$ for four electrons, and so forth. Addition of two electron spins to give the allowed values $S = 0$ and $S = 1$ is illustrated in Figure 6.3.† Finally the total orbital ($L$) and spin ($S$) momenta for the atom are combined to give a resultant angular momentum specified by the quantum number $J$. The rules governing this combination are similar to the foregoing. Addition of the vectors of magnitudes $(h/2\pi)\ \sqrt{L(L+1)}$ and $(h/2\pi)\ \sqrt{S(S+1)}$ must be performed so as to give a resultant magnitude $(h/2\pi)\ \sqrt{J(J+1)}$. $J$ must be an integer or zero when $S$ is integral; it must be a half-integer when $S$ is half-integral.

The manner in which quantum states are occupied by atomic electrons, as governed by the Pauli principle, is shown in Table 6.1 for the first three atomic shells. There are two distinct detailed states in the first completed shell, eight in the second, eighteen in the third, and so forth. Orientations of the angular momenta in a completed shell are dictated by the Pauli principle as indicated by the values of $m_\ell$ and $m_s$ in Table 6.1. When this restriction is combined with the rules for R-S coupling an interesting result emerges. For any completed shell the individual angular momenta must add vectorially to give a total of zero.‡ Thus the completed shells contribute nothing to the values of $L$, $S$, and $J$. These

---

† The two situations shown in Figure 6.3 are described commonly as antiparallel and parallel spins. In the "parallel" case ($S = 1$) the individual spin vectors are only crudely parallel; in the opposite case the vectors are strictly antiparallel.
‡ The same is true for a completed subshell, such as the set of six "$3p$" electrons in the $M$ shell.

quantum numbers can be computed from the contributions of the valence electrons alone.

Given a particular value of $S$, the orientation of this total spin vector can have a set of quantized values relative to an external magnetic field. These orientations are indicated by a number $M_S$; the relationship between $M_S$ and $S$ is like that between $m_\ell$ and $\ell$ when $S$ is integral and like that between $m_s$ and $s$ when $S$ is half-integral. The number of different orientations corresponding to the value of $S$ is called the multiplicity (singlet, doublet, et cetera) of the system; it is equal to $2S + 1$. These relationships and designations are shown in Table 6.2. Note that there is no such thing as a "triplet electron"; only a triplet state involving an even number of electrons.

The foregoing description of atomic electron states has not dealt with the spatial distributions of the electrons. The position of an electron (or of any particle) is described by a probability amplitude, $\Psi$, which is a function of the space coordinates and of time. The square of $\Psi$ (more generally, $\Psi$ multiplied by its complex conjugate) is the positional probability density; it measures the expectation of finding the electron in a particular segment of space and time. The probability distribution of a particle has a wavelike character, and the function $\Psi$ is correspondingly called a wave function. For a particle in a stationary state, such as an atomic electron in a certain quantum state, $\Psi$ describes a standing wave. In such a case the spatial dependence of $\Psi^2$ does not vary with time. This fixed distribution pattern, or orbital, maps the probability density of the particle. The $\Psi$ function of a moving particle has the properties of a propagated wave; in this case the spatial distribution of probability density changes with time. The probability density, being given by $\Psi^2$, is independent of whether $\Psi$ is positive or negative. The sign of $\Psi$ serves to specify the phase of the wave function and is thus involved in describing the dynamic properties of the wave. A complete description of an electron must include its spin orientation, and so $\Psi$ also contains a "spin factor" that affects its sign.

Wave functions for various states of atomic electrons are sketched crudely in Figure 6.4. In regions hatched vertically $\Psi$ is positive, and

TABLE 6.2. Quantization of the axial component of the total electron spin angular momentum of an atom.

| $S$ | $M_S$ | Multiplicity |
|---|---|---|
| 0 | 0 | singlet |
| $\frac{1}{2}$ | $\frac{1}{2}, -\frac{1}{2}$ | doublet |
| 1 | $1, 0, -1$ | triplet |
| $\frac{3}{2}$ | $\frac{3}{2}, \frac{1}{2}, -\frac{1}{2}, -\frac{3}{2}$ | quartet |

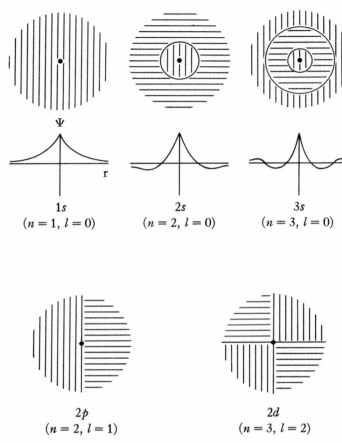

FIGURE 6.4. *Distribution of the wave function (that is, the probability amplitude)* Ψ *for an atomic electron in various quantum states. Regions of positive and negative* Ψ *are distinguished by vertical and horizontal shading;* Ψ *is zero at the boundary between opposite regions. The square of* Ψ *gives the probability density for finding the electron at a given point. The atomic nucleus is at the center of each diagram.*

in those ruled horizontally Ψ is negative. Which region is positive and which is negative is arbitrary in these drawings. The boundaries between regions of positive and negative Ψ are nodes where Ψ² is zero. Note that the wave functions of *s* states, corresponding to zero angular momentum, are functions of the radial coordinate only, whereas the wave functions of *p* and *d* states show angular as well as radial dependence.

A wave function is symmetric or antisymmetric with respect to an operation according to whether its sign is unchanged or reversed by that operation. Two operations are of special importance in the formulation of atomic theory. One of these is inversion (that is, reflection in the center of mass, or changing the signs of all the coordinates in a frame of reference whose origin is at the center of mass). The symmetry of $\Psi$ under this operation defines the parity of the system: odd if $\Psi$ is antisymmetric and even if $\Psi$ is symmetric. The selection rules that govern electronic transitions (see Section 6.2) are based on the parity of the system's wave function. Another operation, the interchange of two electrons in an atomic system, provides a basis for a generalized statement of the Pauli principle: only those atomic states are allowed for which the total wave function (of all the electrons) is antisymmetric with respect to the interchange of any two electrons.† In this form the Pauli principle will help in elucidating the probabilities of transitions between singlet ($S = 0$) and triplet ($S = 1$) states.

## 6.2 Electronic Excited States and Transitions in Atoms

The electrons in an atom will tend to occupy the states of lowest energy allowed by the Pauli principle. The energy of a state is specified mainly by the quantum number $n$, but is modified considerably by electrostatic and magnetic interactions between the electrons. As a result the sequence of increasing energy does not always parallel the increase in the quantum number $n$. In potassium the $4s$ state ($n = 4$, $\ell = 0$) is lower in energy than any of the $3d$ ($n = 3, \ell = 2$) states, and so the final (valence) electron occupies the $N$ shell ($n = 4$) rather than the uncompleted $M$ shell. States that can be discriminated only through their interaction with an external field, such as the three orientations ($M_S$-values) of a triplet state, are degenerate; in the absence of the applied field they all have the same energy. It is meaningless to say which of these states is being occupied until the degeneracy has been removed by application of the external field.

An atom is in its electronic ground state when all of its electrons are in the lowest-energy states available. Promotion of any electron to a higher-energy state corresponds to excitation of the atom. The increment in energy must of course be gained from the surroundings of the atom, characteristically through the absorption of a quantum of electromagnetic radiation. By equating the energy increment to the energy of the absorbed quantum, $\Delta E = h\nu = hc/\lambda$ where $\lambda$ and $\nu$ are the wavelength and frequency of the radiation and $c$ is the speed of light in vacuum. In the reverse transition, from the excited state to the ground state, a quantum of the same energy is emitted. The polarization of the absorbed and emitted light is determined by the orientation of the dipole oscillation that accompanies the transition (see the next paragraph).

† If the wave function were symmetric under permutation of two electrons, those two electrons would be in the same detailed quantum state.

The possible variety of such transitions is restricted by certain selection rules, the most important rule being that the parity of the total wave function must change from odd to even or vice versa. Only then does the charge distribution show, during the transition, a dipole oscillation that corresponds to the absorption or emission of a quantum of energy.[†] This symmetry requirement can be expressed in terms of $J$, the quantum number for total angular momentum: In any transition $J$ must change by $\pm 1$ or 0, but not all cases of $\Delta J = 0$ are allowed. A transition between two states having $J = 0$ is always forbidden.

Collisions between atoms can spoil the perfectly even or odd parity (by spoiling the positional symmetry of the electron distribution) and cause "forbidden" transitions to be detectable.

Additional selection rules, less rigid than the foregoing, have to do with the spin and positional components of the wave function separately and are expressed in terms of the quantum numbers $S$ and $L$. In the lighter elements, for which R-S coupling gives a good approximation, there is very little interaction between the spin magnetic moment of an electron and the orbital magnetic moment of the same and other electrons. Also the interaction (necessarily magnetic) between the electron spin and an external radiation field is far weaker than the electric interaction between the atomic electrons and the radiation. There is therefore very little force tending to change the spin orientation during a transition in a light atom, and as a rule transitions involving a change in the total spin quantum number $S$ are not favored. In heavy atoms the outer electrons have greater momenta and their spin interacts more strongly with the magnetic moments of the other electrons and the nucleus. The rule prohibiting a change in multiplicity is then less forceful, and intense spectral lines corresponding to singlet-triplet transitions can be observed (the mercury line at 254 $m\mu$ falls in this category).

The generalized Pauli principle, which allows only those states whose wave functions are antisymmetric under the interchange of any two electrons, has a bearing on the occurrence of transitions in which $S$ changes. The antisymmetric property involves both the positional and the spin components of the wave function. If antisymmetry (under electron interchange) is to be preserved in the complete wave function, any change of this property in the spin component must be compensated by a complementary change in the positional component. Compensation of this kind is a requisite for transitions between singlet and triplet states. In heavy atoms, or in light atoms subjected to collisions, the spin and positional components of the total wave function become mixed and lose their individual symmetry properties. The requirement of the Pauli principle

[†] There are "weakly allowed" transitions that violate this rule, in which the change in charge distribution corresponds to an oscillating quadrupole or higher multipole.

can then be met in a greater variety of ways, and some kinds of singlet-triplet transitions become facilitated.

As long as the spin-orbital interactions are very weak and transitions involving a change in $S$ are forbidden, the orbital quantum number $L$ will obey selection rules similar to those for $J$. But the rules for $J$ are based rigidly on the symmetry property of parity whereas those for $L$ rest on the approximation of weak spin interactions.

There is no selection rule involving the quantum number $n$, but radiative transitions in which $n$ does not change are uncommon.

The selection rules governing a transition in one direction apply equally to a transition in the opposite direction. Thus if we consider transitions between a ground state $G$ and an excited state $E$ for an atom in a radiation field, the probability of excitation ($G \rightarrow E$ with absorption of a quantum of energy) is proportional to that of de-excitation ($E \rightarrow G$; emission of a quantum). A high transition probability is then manifested by intense absorption of energy in the ground state, intense emission from the excited state, and a short lifetime of the excited state. The probability of a transition allowed by the parity rule is given by

$$P = \text{const.} \times \mid \int \Psi^*_G M \Psi_E \, dv \mid^2. \qquad [6.2.1]$$

In this formula $\Psi_G$ and $\Psi_E$ are the wave functions of the two states involved in the transition ($\Psi^*_G$ is the complex conjugate of $\Psi_G$), and the integration is performed over all space. $M$ is the quantum-mechanical dipole moment operator; in the integral of Equation [6.2.1] it describes the change in electric dipole moment that accompanies the transition. Equation [6.2.1] shows that the transition probability will be low if there is little spatial overlap between the wave functions for the two states. The probability will also be low if the change in dipole moment is small. The lifetime of an atom in the excited state is inversely proportional to the transition probability.

# 7. Excited States in Organic Molecules

## 7.1 Molecular Electron Orbitals

WHEN ATOMS combine to form molecules the atomic electrons become involved in a wide range of new interactions. An electron is in the force field of more than one nucleus, and the nuclei are not stationary with respect to each other. The principles that govern atomic states can be extended to molecules but a detailed description of molecular states becomes hopelessly complicated. We shall consider only a few aspects of molecular excitations that are especially pertinent to the problems of photosynthesis.

Every atomic state is degenerate; it is accompanied by at least one other state having the same energy in the absence of external forces. The two $1s$ electrons of the $K$ shell differ only in their spin magnetic quantum number; the $2p$ states have sixfold degeneracy (three values of $m_l$ and two $m_s$ values for each of these). The different states in a degenerate set interact differently with an external field and thereby acquire different values of energy. Single lines in atomic spectra thus become split, by a magnetic field, into multiplets (Zeeman effect). Transitions among the multiplet levels become possible; observation of such transitions falls in the province of microwave spectroscopy.

In a molecule the surroundings of any one atom are equivalent to a complicated external electromagnetic field. Degenerate atomic states are resolved through interactions with this field, and the number of distinct energy levels and possible transitions is increased. More significantly, an electron becomes involved with more than one nucleus. A variety of orbitals embracing two or more nuclei are possible, and the splitting of formerly degenerate energy levels becomes grosser and more prolific. The transitions from ground state energy levels in atoms almost always require energies of several electron volts and hence involve ultraviolet quanta. In molecules the proliferation of energy levels affords many transitions in the visible and infrared. A single atomic ground state can be split into a molecular ground (normally occupied) state and one or more low-lying excited (normally unoccupied) levels; transitions into these molecular excited states require far less energy than transitions into the higher "atomic" levels. This state of affairs is depicted in simplified form in Figure 7.1. In this figure the energy increments $\Delta E_1$ and $\Delta E_2$ correspond to "atomic" and "molecular" transitions respectively.

For molecular electrons that interact with two or more atomic nuclei the orbitals are profitably described in terms of a fusion of atomic orbitals. In the case of a diatomic molecule the internuclear axis provides a simple frame of reference for considerations of symmetry. Orbitals can then be classified according to the angular momentum about this axis in analogy with the classification of angular momenta about a nucleus in a single atom. By following this procedure one can describe $\sigma, \pi, \delta, \ldots$ orbitals in molecules, analogous to $s, p, d, \ldots$ orbitals in atoms. The wave function for a $\sigma$ orbital is axially symmetric, just as that for an $s$ orbital is spherically symmetric. In atoms the $s$, $p$, and $d$ states correspond to values of 0, 1, and 2 for the quantum number $\ell$. In a diatomic molecule an analogous quantum number, $\lambda$, has values of 0, 1, and 2 for the $\sigma$, $\pi$, and $\delta$ states.

If the molecule is homonuclear there is a center of symmetry as well as an axis of symmetry. Wave functions can then be symmetric or anti-symmetric with respect to reflection in this center, that is, they can be described as having even or odd parity. The selection rules for atoms can then be carried over: if spin-orbital interaction is weak, $\lambda$ must change by $\pm 1$ or 0 in a transition. In a transition between two $\pi$ states, for which $\Delta\lambda = 0$, the dipole oscillation is parallel to the internuclear axis. If $\Delta\lambda = \pm 1$ the oscillation is perpendicular to the axis. A $\pi$-$\pi$ transition must, from the selection principle, involve a change from even to odd parity or vice versa. Such a transition can be especially intense because a strong dipole oscillation is combined with a high degree of overlap between the two wave functions. In a heteronuclear molecule there is no geometrical center of symmetry. Symmetry classifications are then more complicated and the prediction of favored and unfavored transitions becomes more difficult.

In addition to the $\sigma, \pi, \delta, \ldots$ orbitals in molecules there are so-called $n$ orbitals that resemble atomic orbitals embedded in the molecule. An $n$ electron is confined to the neighborhood of one nucleus and interacts little with the other nuclei. The wave functions of the $n$ orbitals in a molecular atom are scarcely different from their counterparts in the isolated atom.

The structure of formaldehyde, $H_2C{=}O$, lends itself well to a description of $n$, $\sigma$, and $\pi$ orbitals.  The C atom has in its outer shell two $2s$ electrons that interact with the H atoms and two $2p$ electrons that bond the O atom through $\sigma$ and $\pi$ orbitals.  Two of the $2p$ electrons of the O atom share these orbitals.  The other $2p$ electrons and the $2s$ electrons in

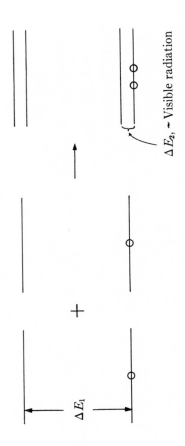

FIGURE 7.1.   *An illustration of the proliferation of energy levels and the generation of low-lying unoccupied states that occurs when atoms interact to form molecules.*

Formaldehyde

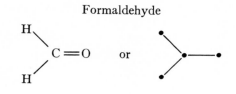

$n$ Orbitals

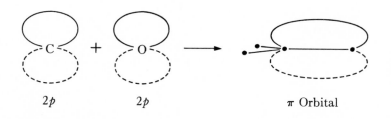

FIGURE 7.2. *Molecular electron orbitals in formaldehyde. The profiles of the wave functions* ($\Psi$) *are sketched crudely around the atoms involved in the orbitals. Positive and negative regions are indicated by solid and dashed curves; the sign is arbitrary. In the sketch of a* $\pi$ *orbital the molecular plane is perpendicular to the paper.*

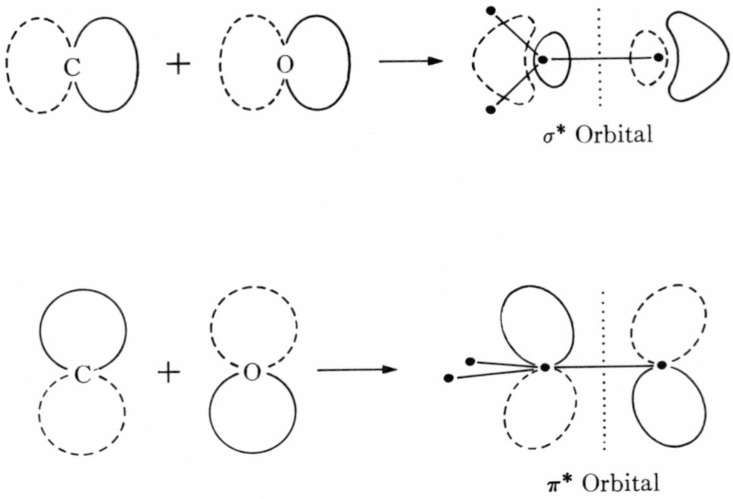

σ* Orbital

π* Orbital

FIGURE 7.3. *Antibonding orbitals representing excited states in formaldehyde. Wave functions are sketched as in Figure 7.2. The dotted lines show the presence of nodes ($\Psi = 0$) between the C and O atoms.*

the O atom remain localized in $n$ orbitals. The $\sigma$ and $\pi$ orbitals can be visualized as resulting from a fusion of the atomic $2p$ orbitals, as shown in Figure 7.2. In this figure the wave functions are sketched with solid lines in their positive regions and dashed lines in their negative regions. The $2p$ orbitals aligned with the C—O axis give rise to a $\sigma$ orbital; those perpendicular to the molecular plane yield a $\pi$ orbital. The $2p$ orbital of oxygen that lies in the molecular plane, but perpendicular to the C—O axis, remains isolated and thus becomes an $n$ orbital. The $2s$ orbital of oxygen constitutes another $n$ orbital.

In this imagined fusion the orientation of one of the $2p$ orbitals can be reversed and a new set of $\sigma$ and $\pi$ orbitals generated, as shown in Figure 7.3. For these new $\sigma$ and $\pi$ orbitals the wave function has a node ($\Psi^2 = 0$) between the C and O atoms and the orbitals are antibonding rather than bonding. The higher energy levels of these antibonding orbitals places them in the category of excited states rather than ground states; the symbols $\sigma^*$ and $\pi^*$ are used to denote this condition.

In this example the interaction between $2p$ states is strongest in the axial direction. The $\sigma$ and $\sigma^*$ states therefore have the lowest and highest energy, respectively. The $\pi$ and $\pi^*$ states are intermediate between these, and the relatively unperturbed $n$ state derived from a $2p$ state lies between the $\pi$ and $\pi^*$ levels. The $2s$-derived $n$ state is so firmly bound to the O atom that it lies far below the other levels and need not be considered in

connection with molecular excitations.    An energy level diagram for the
$\sigma$, $\pi$, $n(2p)$, $\pi^*$, and $\sigma^*$ orbitals is shown in Figure 7.4.    There are six electrons (two $2p$ electrons from carbon and four from oxygen) available to
occupy these orbitals, and two can occupy a single orbital by having
oppositely directed spins.    As a result the $\sigma$, $\pi$ and $n$ orbitals are occupied
and the $\pi^*$ and $\sigma^*$ orbitals are vacant when the molecule is in its ground
state.

The pairwise filling of molecular orbitals is a characteristic of covalent
bonding.    Since the spins of each pair must be antiparallel, the total spin
angular momentum is zero and the ground states of organic molecules are
singlet states.    Only under excitation, charge-transfer, or radical formation can unpaired electron spins (and hence multiplet states) arise.    The
doublet state of an unpaired electron in an organic radical is resolved into
two energy levels in the presence of a magnetic field; transitions between
the two levels can then be promoted by electromagnetic radiation.    With
the magnetic field strengths available in the laboratory the energy gap
corresponds to microwave quanta.    The technique of ESR spectroscopy
is the observation of this kind of resonance absorption of microwave
energy.    Triplet states in excited molecules are more difficult to observe
with this technique because the alignment of spins in a collection of molecules shows considerable statistical variation and the microwave absorption band is correspondingly broad and shallow.

In an organic molecule containing an extensive system of alternating
single and double bonds (such as benzene, carotene, or Chl) the conjugated
atoms generate $\pi$ orbitals that extend throughout the region of conjugation.    These orbitals can be thought to arise from a fusion of adjacent
$2p$ orbitals.    The $2p$ orbitals can be parallel or antiparallel (as in Figures
7.2 and 7.3 respectively); different permutations of this condition will
yield as many distinct $\pi$ orbitals as there are atoms in the conjugated

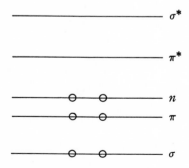

FIGURE 7.4.    *Energy levels of the orbitals shown in Figures 7.2 and 7.3.    The three
lowest states are occupied, each orbital having two electrons with opposite spins.*

system. The $\pi$ orbital of lowest energy is the one that is completely bonding, arising from a fusion of $2p$ orbitals that are all parallel. The greater the number of nodes in the wave function, arising from fusion of adjacent antiparallel $2p$ orbitals, the higher the energy of the resulting $\pi$ orbital.

## 7.2  Molecular Electronic Transitions

Transitions of electrons from one molecular orbital to another, such as from $\pi$ to $\pi^*$ or from $n$ to $\pi^*$, are called $\pi\pi^*$ or $n\pi^*$ (et cetera) transitions. In the absence of notation to the contrary these are assumed to be singlet transitions, that is, ones in which the spin of the excited electron remains coupled to that of its unexcited partner in the antiparallel orientation. These transitions can be portrayed in an energy level diagram showing the shifts of electrons into new orbitals. The upper half of Figure 7.5 shows such a diagram for the following sequence of events. (1) The promotion of a $\pi$ electron to a $\pi^*$ orbital. (2) The transfer of an electron from the $n$ orbital to the partly vacated $\pi$ orbital (the net result of these two steps is the promotion of an $n$ electron to the $\pi^*$ orbital). (3) The fall of the $\pi^*$ electron into the vacancy in the $n$ orbital. The same events are repre-

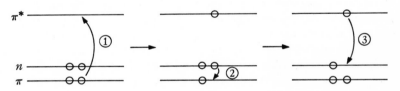

Energy level diagram

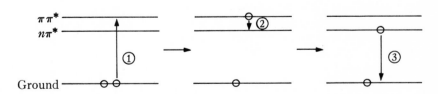

Transition diagram

FIGURE 7.5.  *Energy level and transition diagrams for a molecule such as formaldehyde. Three events are represented: promotion of an electron from the $\pi$ to the $\pi^*$ orbital, transfer of an electron from the n to the $\pi$ orbital, and a transition of the $\pi^*$ electron to the n orbital. In terms of molecular states these events are $\pi\pi^*$ excitation, $\pi\pi^* \to n\pi^*$ interconversion, and de-excitation from $n\pi^*$ to ground.*

sented more conveniently and more correctly by a transition diagram (lower half of Figure 7.5). This diagram shows the energy levels of the ground state and the various excited states of the molecule as a whole. Thus the $n\pi^*$ state means the state in which an electron has been promoted from the $n$ orbital to the $\pi^*$ orbital. Events (1), (2), and (3) as portrayed in the energy level diagram are indicated as transitions between molecular levels in the transition diagram. (1) is a $\pi\pi^*$ excitation; (2) is a $\pi\pi^* \rightarrow n\pi^*$ interconversion (which, by the way, is usually a forbidden transition); and (3) is a de-excitation from $n\pi^*$ to ground.

In transition diagrams no attempt is made to show the fates of individual electrons in detail. The energy level diagram (as shown in Figure 7.5, top) is not strictly correct because it treats the energy levels as though they were independent of their state of occupancy. Actually the energy of an electron in the $\pi^*$ orbital will depend slightly on whether the $\pi$ or the $n$ orbital has been vacated. The $n$ and $\pi$ levels are affected similarly. These effects can be encompassed in the transition diagram without making the diagram more complicated, simply by setting the $\pi\pi^*$ and $n\pi^*$ states at suitable heights above the ground level. This is so because the transition diagram describes the energies of molecular states and not of individual electrons.

The transitions between low-lying molecular states are of first importance in photochemistry and optical spectroscopy because the energy gaps are in the range of visible and near ultraviolet quanta. The most intense absorption bands in molecular spectra correspond to $\pi\pi^*$ transitions; these are highly favored because of the strong dipole oscillation and the high degree of overlap between the ground and excited state wave functions. The $\pi$ and $\pi^*$ orbitals differ in their symmetry but cover approximately the same region of the molecule. The intrinsic lifetimes of $\pi\pi^*$ excited states are commonly about $10^{-8}$ sec.

In an $n\pi^*$ transition an electron vacates a localized orbital and enters a nearby delocalized orbital. The spatial overlap between the localized ($n$) and delocalized ($\pi^*$) orbitals is poor and the transition probability is correspondingly low. As a result the absorption bands of $n\pi^*$ transitions are ten- to one hundred-fold less intense than those of $\pi\pi^*$ transitions. The intrinsic lifetimes of $n\pi^*$ states are greater than those of $\pi\pi^*$ states by the same factor.

Another important characteristic of $n\pi^*$ states is their high degree of polarization, due to the large electron displacement attending the transition. It can be expected that this polarization will give the $n\pi^*$-excited molecule considerable reactivity as an electron donor or acceptor. The molecule should then be especially susceptible to intermolecular processes that lead to de-excitation (quenching processes). As a result the actual lifetime of an $n\pi^*$ state may be far less than its intrinsic or natural lifetime.

As a result of the combination of high polarization and long natural lifetime the $n\pi^*$ excited state has been regarded as potentially important in the initiation of photochemistry. Concrete evidence on this point remains meager. Nevertheless the hypothetical participation of $n\pi^*$ states in Chl has been invoked to account for the optical properties of Chl *in vitro*. These states have also played an interesting role in the development of theories of photosynthesis (see Chapter 13).

The foregoing discussion has been confined to transitions between singlet states, in which the spin of an excited electron remains antiparallel to that of its ground-state partner. In many cases (especially in $\pi\pi^*$ transitions) the spin of an electron undergoing excitation is coupled more closely to that of its partner than to any other magnetic forces in its environment. The spin of the excited electron must then be either antiparallel or parallel to that of its partner. The parallel orientation, producing a triplet state, is improbable for the reasons described in Section 6.2.

There corresponds to every singlet excited state, then, a less probable triplet excited state in which the spin of an electron has become reversed during excitation. Transitions from the ground (singlet) state to excited triplet states are usually about $10^5$-fold less likely than those to excited singlet states; the lifetimes of triplet states are typically of the order of milliseconds. The triplet excited states have special importance in the mediation of photochemistry because of their long lifetime and their magnetic moment. We shall see in Chapter 8 that triplets are involved in the photochemistry of Chl *in vitro;* their role in photosynthesis is far less certain.

Triplet states are of lower energy than their singlet counterparts because the excited electron and its partner have parallel spins. The difference in energy results mainly from a resonance effect associated with interchange of the two electrons. The more closely coupled the two electrons are, the greater is the energy difference between the singlet and the triplet state.

The spin moment of an excited electron always interacts to some extent with magnetic forces other than the spin moment of its ground-state partner. Orientations not strictly antiparallel or parallel are established, and the excitation acquires a mixed singlet-triplet character. Singlet and triplet excited states are only *predominantly* singlet and triplet respectively. A "pure triplet" state would indeed be forbidden, and the allowedness of a triplet excited state can be ascribed to a small "singlet component" in the otherwise triplet wave function. The principal magnetic forces that disrupt the spin-spin coupling of a pair of electrons are the orbital magnetic moments of electrons and atomic nuclei.[†] The greater

† From our point of view the sun appears to orbit the earth. Similarly, as "seen" by a spinning electron, a nucleus appears to move in an orbit around the electron. From this point of view the nucleus has an orbital magnetic moment proportional to its charge.

the spin-orbital coupling, and the weaker the spin-spin coupling, the more the likelihood of a singlet→triplet transition.

The spin-orbital coupling is stronger and the spin-spin coupling weaker in excited states than in ground states, simply because the excited electron occupies an orbital different from that of its partner. For this reason the entry of a molecule into a triplet state is far more likely to occur from an excited singlet state than from the ground state in a direct excitation. The greater spin-orbital coupling and lesser spin-spin coupling is especially marked in $n\pi^*$ singlet states, as contrasted with $\pi\pi^*$ states. Furthermore the $n\pi^*$ states are intrinsically longer lived than the $\pi\pi^*$ states. The former should therefore be particularly able to mediate the entry into a triplet state. This will not be the case, however, if the actual lifetime of an $n\pi^*$ state is shortened as a result of quenching processes.

Several other factors can be expected to encourage singlet-triplet transitions. Among these are collisions that disrupt molecular symmetry and the proximity of heavy nuclei (see Section 6.2).

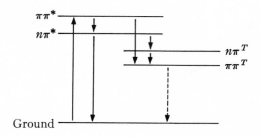

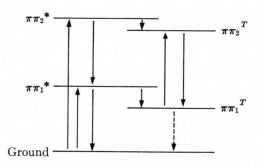

FIGURE 7.6. *Transition diagrams including the triplet (for example, $\pi\pi^T$) states as well as the singlet states. Direct transitions between the triplet states and the ground state are extremely improbable.*

The transition from a triplet state to a higher excited triplet state is not forbidden because no realignment of the spin is involved. Such transitions appear as bands in the absorption spectra of molecules that have been placed in the lowest triplet state.

The energy gap between an $n\pi^*$ (singlet) state and the corresponding $n\pi^T$ (triplet) state is less than that between $\pi\pi^*$ and $\pi\pi^T$ since the spin coupling is less in the former case. Figure 7.6 shows some paths of excitation and de-excitation; first for an $n\pi^*$ and a $\pi\pi^*$ state and the corresponding triplet states, second for a pair of $\pi\pi^*$ states and their triplet counterparts. The less favored pathways are omitted, except for the return from the lowest triplet state to ground (shown as a dashed arrow).

## 7.3  Absorption and Emission of Light

Electronic transitions in molecules are studied by observing optical absorption and emission spectra. The term fluorescence is applied to the emission, usually of a lifetime less than about $10^{-8}$ sec, that accompanies "allowed" radiative transitions such as the return from $\pi\pi^*$ to ground. Radiative de-excitations from metastable states such as triplets are manifested by the longer lived phosphorescence (or luminescence, or delayed light emission). The distinction between fluorescence and phosphorescence is based on whether the emission is associated with singlet or metastable states. Although the lifetime is usually a satisfactory criterion, there are exceptional cases of long-lived fluorescence and short-lived phosphorescence (see later in this section).

The absorption and emission spectra of atoms are typically "line spectra"; each line represents a unique value of the difference in energy between two states. This shows that the electronic energy levels in atoms are sharply defined. The situation is different with molecules; several factors cause the electronic energy levels to be split into sublevels and thus to become diffuse. Correspondingly, the spectra of absorption and emission are characterized by broad bands rather than by sharp lines. In molecular aggregates the electric and collisional interactions among the molecules can cause broadening of the energy levels in a variety of ways. In isolated molecules the main sources of broadening are the vibrations and rotations of the atomic nuclei.

Because of nuclear movements an electronic state in a molecule is subdivided into a quantized set of vibrational substates and these in turn are divided into rotational "sub-substates." The difference in energy between two successive vibrational levels (within a single electronic level) is typically several times smaller than the energy gap between two electronic levels, and the rotational levels are in turn spaced ten- to one hundred-fold closer together than the vibrational levels. We shall con-

sider the way that electronic transitions are affected by nuclear vibrations. The additional effect of rotations can be inferred from these considerations.

The role of nuclear vibrations in molecular spectroscopy can be appreciated by examining the behavior of an idealized diatomic molecule. The two nuclei of the molecule are linked by the (covalent) bonding electrons; the nature of the binding is determined by the orbitals of these electrons and by the mutual electrostatic repulsion of the nuclei. Let us imagine first that the nuclei can be regarded as particles connected by a spring obeying Hooke's Law. The nuclei then comprise a simple harmonic oscillator, for which the potential energy of vibration is a parabolic function of the distance $r$ separating the nuclei. This relationship between vibrational potential energy and nuclear separation is shown by the curved line in Figure 7.7 for a particular electronic state (such as the ground state). In accordance with quantum theory the vibrational energy of such a system is restricted to a set of values given by $E_{\text{vib.}} = \text{const.} \times (v + \frac{1}{2})$, where the vibrational quantum number $v$ can be 0, 1, 2, . . . . The first four of these vibrational levels are shown by the horizontal lines in Figure 7.7. If the molecule is in its third vibrational level ($v = 2$) its state is represented by the horizontal line segment between $A$ and $C$. In classical

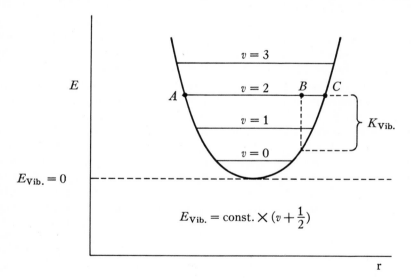

FIGURE 7.7. *Potential energy diagram for a diatomic molecule consisting of two nuclei bound in the manner of an harmonic oscillator. The curved line shows the potential energy as a function of the internuclear distance r. The quantized vibrational states are shown by horizontal lines. For the molecule in its third vibrational state (v = 2) the vibrational energy is, in classical terms, all potential for the values of r corresponding to points A and C. At B the energy is part kinetic as shown.*

terms a complete nuclear oscillation can be visualized as the movement of a point on that line segment, say from $A$ to $C$ and back again. At point $A$ the vibrational energy is all potential, as in a pendulum at one extreme of its swing. At point $B$ part of the energy is kinetic; this part is indicated (as $K_{vib.}$) by the vertical distance from $B$ to the potential energy curve. In this way a single point on the diagram specifies three things: the energy of the molecule, the internuclear distance $r$, and the momenta of the nuclei as implied by the kinetic energy of vibration. Thus a point on the diagram represents a hypothetical instant at which the nuclei have certain positions and momenta.†

The lifetime of an electronic excited state is usually greater than $10^{-9}$ sec, but the time actually spent in a transition (during the process of excitation or de-excitation) is far less. It is of the same order as the period of vibration of the absorbed or emitted quantum; about $10^{-15}$ sec. A nuclear vibration is much slower, requiring about $10^{-13}$ sec, and a rotation is still more ponderous. These facts are expressed by the Franck-Condon principle: neither the positions nor the momenta of the atomic nuclei change appreciably during an electronic transition in a molecule.

When used in conjunction with a nuclear potential energy diagram the Franck-Condon principle gives immediate insight into the nature of absorption and fluorescence spectra. Consider a pair of vibrational potential energy curves, one for a molecule in its ground state and the other for the first excited state, as shown in Figure 7.8 (in this example the parabolic shape corresponding to simple harmonic oscillation is abandoned in favor of a more realistic shape). One curve is placed far enough above the other to account for the difference in the electronic energy levels. One requirement of the Franck-Condon principle is that the nuclear separation $r$ does not change during an electronic transition. This means that transitions are represented by vertical line segments in Figure 7-8. The transition $B \rightarrow B'$ is a change from the lowest vibrational level of the electronic ground state to the third level of the excited state. The energy needed for this change, represented by the distance from $B$ to $B'$, is absorbed as a quantum of radiation. In the opposite transition, from $B'$ to $B$, a fluorescent quantum of the same energy would be emitted.

The other Franck-Condon requirement, that the nuclear momenta do not change, dictates that the kinetic component of the vibrational energy is the same before and after a transition. This necessitates a relationship between the end points ($A$ and $A'$, et cetera) of the vertical line segments.

† This descent to classical analogies is inadmissible in quantum theory; for one thing we have violated the uncertainty principle by implying that both the positions and the momenta of the nuclei can be specified with certainty at a given instant. Such breaches of rigor can be tolerated if they are recognized and if they afford a lucid visualization of the processes being described.

Points $A$, $B$, and $D$ in the figure all lie on the lower potential energy curve. They all represent instants when the nuclei are at rest (at one extreme or the other of their oscillation). A transition from any one of these points must then terminate at a point ($A'$, $B'$, and $D'$ respectively) on the upper potential curve, so that the nuclei are still at rest just after the transition. The point $C$ represents a condition in which the nuclei have some kinetic energy; a transition from this state must be to a state $C'$ such that the nuclei retain the same kinetic energy. The nuclear kinetic energy is given by the vertical distance from $C'$ to the upper potential curve, or from $C$ to the lower curve, as indicated by the hatched lines.

An electronic transition, governed by the Franck-Condon principle and involving a change in the vibrational level (for example, $B \rightarrow B'$ in

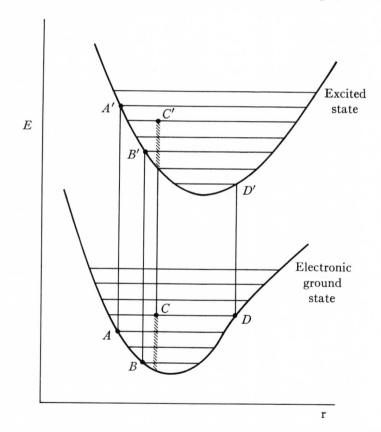

FIGURE 7.8. *Energy diagram for a diatomic molecule in its ground state and in an electronic excited state. Transitions compatible with the Franck-Condon principle (see text) are shown by the vertical lines.*

Figure 7.8), can be visualized through a simple classical analogy.    Imagine a pendulum made of a weight supported by a string.    Suppose that the string is suddenly clamped somewhere along its length while the pendulum is swinging.    The length of the swinging part is thereby reduced abruptly and the pendulum enters a new vibrational mode characterized by a higher frequency.    During the transition (in the short time required to clamp the string) neither the position nor the momentum of the weight changes appreciably.

Several conclusions can be drawn from Figure 7.8.    For a transition to be possible, the final state as determined by the Franck-Condon principle must coincide with one of the vibrational energy levels.    As drawn in the figure, point $A'$ is at the intersection of the potential curve and an energy level.    Had the line $AA'$ intercepted the upper potential curve between two energy levels, the transition $A \rightarrow A'$ would not have been possible.    The probabilities of transitions are therefore influenced by the density of vibrational levels and the extent to which these levels are broadened into sets of rotational sublevels.    Which of the various vibrational levels can be entered in a transition is governed by the state being vacated and by the dictates of the Franck-Condon principle.

The line segments $AA'$, $BB'$, $CC'$, and $DD'$ are of unequal lengths and thus represent transitions of different energies.    A band in an absorption (or fluorescence) spectrum is compounded out of an infinitude of such transitions, weighted according to their relative probabilities.    Transitions of the kind $A \rightarrow A'$, $B \rightarrow B'$, and $D \rightarrow D'$ (or vice versa) are more likely than the $C \rightarrow C'$ kind.    The reason is that a molecule spends most of its time in a state in which the nuclei are nearly at rest.    To draw an analogy, a pendulum spends most of its time near the two extremes of its oscillation because it is moving most slowly when it is near these extreme positions.

The main factor governing the shapes of absorption and fluorescence bands in molecules is the statistical distribution of molecules among the vibrational levels.    In a collection of molecules in the electronic ground state at low temperature the majority will be in the lowest vibrational states.    Excitations will be predominantly from these lower levels of the ground state into higher vibrational levels of the excited state.    Thus the transition $B \rightarrow B'$ in Figure 7.8 is from the lowest ground-state vibrational level to the third level of the excited state.    During the lifetime of the excited state many transitions can occur from one vibrational level to another.[†]    The excited molecules, approaching a thermal distribution among *their* vibrational states, will subside into the lowest vibrational levels.    De-excitations will then be mainly from the lower vibrational levels of the excited state to higher levels in the ground state, as exemplified

† The selection rule for vibrational transitions is that the vibrational quantum number $v$ must change by $\pm 1$.

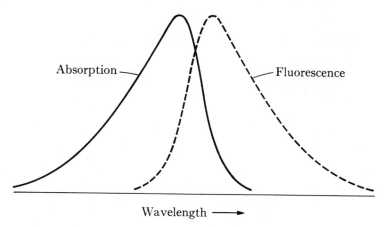

FIGURE 7.9. *Absorption and fluorescence spectra for a molecular electronic transition, as dictated by the Franck-Condon principle.*

by $D' \rightarrow D$ in Figure 7.8. As a result the energy gap for excitation is, on the average, greater than that for de-excitation. Most of the quanta absorbed in excitation are thus of shorter wavelength than those emitted in de-excitation, and an absorption band lies to the short-wave side (Stokes shift) of the corresponding fluorescence band. These considerations, examined in greater detail, account for the mirror-symmetry that is usually seen in absorption and fluorescence bands (see Figure 7.9).

If a molecule is promoted to a higher excited state than the first it will nearly always descend rapidly to the first excited state before returning to the ground state. The descent is made by way of vibrational levels that are connected, from one electronic energy level to the next lower one, by overlap of the vibrational potential curves.† This process of internal conversion is illustrated in Figure 7.10. At the point $P$ the system can be described in two ways: it is in the lowest vibrational level of the second excited state or in the fifth level of the first excited state. The nuclei, instantaneously at rest, are about to begin one or the other of these two modes of oscillation. The descent from $A'$ to $C'$ occurs so rapidly that the alternative pathway, a direct radiative return from the second excited state to ground, is extremely unlikely. The final step, from $C'$ to $C$, is delayed and is accompanied by the emission of fluorescence.

The generality of this situation in organic molecules is shown by the fact that fluorescence is nearly always correlated with the long wave absorption band that represents the transition between the first excited

† The potential curves do not actually cross; they avoid each other while preserving the gross outline of crossed curves (see the inset in Figure 7.10).

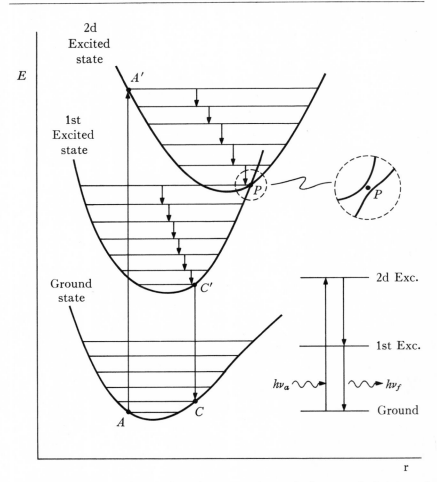

FIGURE 7.10. *Excitation, radiationless conversion to the lowest excited state, and radiative de-excitation in a diatomic molecule. Absorbed and fluorescent quanta are denoted $h\nu_a$ and $h\nu_f$. The potential energy curves for nuclear vibration in the two excited states do not actually cross at the point P; they avoid each other as shown in the inset.*

state and the ground state. Shorter wave absorption bands, representing transitions to higher excited states, are not accompanied by fluorescence bands. The lifetime of the fluorescence indicates the time spent in the lowest excited state before the return to the ground state.

It should be emphasized that the redistribution of molecules among vibrational energy levels, upon which the process of internal conversion depends, involves vibrational transitions and hence the gain or loss of small quanta of energy. Molecular collisions, or lattice vibrations in a molecular crystal, play a major role in promoting these transitions. In an isolated molecule vibrational transitions would have to depend on interactions between different modes of nuclear vibration within the molecule.

The effectiveness of the internal conversion from a higher state to the lowest excited state has an important bearing on the utilization of excitation energy (for example, for photochemistry). It makes little difference whether the primary excitation is to a higher or to a lower excited state; the molecule will enter the lowest excited state before doing anything else. The photochemical effectiveness of an absorbed quantum is therefore independent of its wavelength as long as only one molecular species is under consideration. A quantum of blue light, absorbed in the Soret band of Chl, is photochemically equivalent to a quantum of red light absorbed in the long wave band. Exceptions to this rule might be found under special circumstances, if extremely rapid intermolecular processes can be mediated through the higher excited states.

Ordinarily the nuclear potential energy curves for the ground state and the lowest excited electronic state do not cross. These two states are not connected through overlapping vibrational levels, and a transition between them requires absorption or emission of a quantum of radiation. But during a molecular collision the potential curves may become so distorted that they cross each other temporarily; during this time a pathway exists for radiationless de-excitation *via* the vibrational levels. A conversion to the ground state, analogous to the internal conversion between excited states, is then possible. It is manifested by a quenching of the usual fluorescence and a shortening of the lifetime of the lowest excited state. The "normal" fluorescent return from the lowest excited state to ground can be bypassed in various other ways, all of which cause a shortening of the lifetime and a quenching of the fluorescence. The possibility of such alternative pathways is depicted in Figure 7.11.

Radiationless transitions between $\pi\pi^*$ and $n\pi^*$, or between excited singlet and triplet states, depend on the crossing of potential curves in the same way as the internal conversion from higher to lower singlet states. Such "intercombinations" can be extremely efficient if there is good overlap between vibrational levels of the two states. The transition from $n\pi^*$ to $n\pi^T$ is especially favored because the intrinsic lifetime of $n\pi^*$ is relatively long, because the spin-orbital coupling is strong in $n\pi^*$, and because the energy difference between $n\pi^*$ and $n\pi^T$ is small (giving good overlap between vibrational levels of these states). Thus when the lowest excited singlet state of a molecule is an $n\pi^*$ state, the predominant pathway of de-excitation involves a conversion from $n\pi^*$ to $n\pi^T$. Such molecules exhibit very little fluorescence, and the conversion to the triplet is manifested by a strong phosphorescence at low temperatures. At room

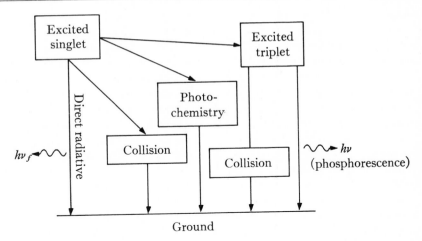

FIGURE 7.11. *Various pathways of de-excitation from an excited singlet state in a molecule.*

temperature the phosphorescence is quenched by collisions that facilitate radiationless return from the triplet state to the ground state. If the lowest excited singlet state is a $\pi\pi^*$ the conversion to the triplet is less probable and fluorescence, accompanying the radiative return from $\pi\pi^*$ to ground, is observed.

Some useful relationships will now be established between the quantum yield of fluorescence, the lifetime of the lowest excited singlet state, and the intensity of the absorption band for transition into that state.

It has already been mentioned that the intrinsic probabilities of absorption and emission are proportional and that the lifetime of an excited state therefore varies inversely as the probability of absorption. The absorption probability is measured by the integrated area under the absorption band. The probabilities of absorption and emission are related by the factor $8\pi hck^3$, where $k$ is the wave number (cm$^{-1}$) for the transition. These and other factors lead to the useful expression

$$\frac{1}{\tau_0} = 2.9 \times 10^{-9}k^2_{\text{ave.}} \int \epsilon \, dk \qquad [7.3.1]$$

for the mean intrinsic lifetime $\tau_0$ of an excited singlet state. The intrinsic lifetime is that which would prevail if fluorescent de-excitation were the only avenue for leaving the excited state. It corresponds to a fluorescence yield of 100% (one quantum emitted for every quantum absorbed in producing the state). In Equation [7.3.1] $k_{\text{ave.}}$ is the mean wave number of the absorption (near the center of the band) and $\int \epsilon \, dk$ is the area under the absorption band plotted as $\epsilon$ *vs.* $k$. The coefficient $\epsilon$ is the molar extinction coefficient as used in specifying optical density:

$$O.D. = \log (I_0/I) = \epsilon C x, \qquad [7.3.2]$$

where $C$ is the concentration of the absorbing substance in moles per liter and $x$ is the optical path length in cm. The shapes of most absorption bands are such that the area $\int \epsilon \, dk$ is approximately equal to the half-width of the band ($\Delta k$) times the value of $\epsilon$ at the peak of absorption ($\epsilon_{max.}$). Equation [7.3.1] can therefore be written in the approximate form

$$\frac{1}{\tau_0} = 3 \times 10^{-9} \, k^2 \, \Delta k \, \epsilon_{max.}, \qquad [7.3.3]$$

where $k$ is the wave number at the peak of absorption and $\Delta k$ is the half-width of the band.

The actual lifetime $\tau$ of the excited state is less than the intrinsic lifetime $\tau_0$ because pathways other than the fluorescent one are available for vacating the state (see Figure 7.11). At the same time that the lifetime is shortened the yield of fluorescence is reduced when these other pathways are followed. The lifetime and yield are related linearly if the quenching processes are first-order with respect to the concentration of molecules in the excited state. In this case

$$\frac{\tau}{\tau_0} = \phi_f, \qquad [7.3.4]$$

where $\phi_f$ is the fluorescence yield corresponding to the actual lifetime $\tau$. By using Equations [7.3.1] and [7.3.4] one can obtain independent determinations of the parameters involved.

The phosphorescence accompanying de-excitation from a triplet state is quenched by paramagnetic substances such as $O_2$ or NO and by oxidizing molecules such as benzoquinone. Interaction between the triplet-state molecule and the quencher affords pathways of radiationless conversion to the ground state. As a result the lifetime of the triplet state can be much less than its intrinsic value of about $10^{-3}$ sec or more. On the other hand the fluorescence associated with a weak singlet transition may be much longer lived than the value of about $10^{-8}$ sec that prevails for the more intense transitions. Lifetimes of phosphorescence and fluorescence can thus overlap considerably.

The quenching action of paramagnetic substances cannot be taken as a reliable criterion for distinguishing phosphorescence from fluorescence, as these same substances will quench the singlet fluorescence by facilitating the conversion of singlet to triplet states. The best criterion is the wavelength of the emitted light. Because the lowest triplet state is of lower energy than the corresponding first excited singlet state, a luminescent quantum emitted in the "triplet → ground" transition is less energetic

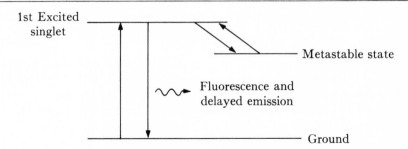

FIGURE 7.12.    *Transitions between the first excited singlet state and a metastable state in a molecule, illustrating a mechanism for the emission of delayed fluorescence.*

than the fluorescent (excited singlet → ground) quantum.    Thus, Chl *b* shows a weak luminescence at 773 m$\mu$ and also at 865 m$\mu$; these probably reflect transitions from $n\pi^T$ and $\pi\pi^T$ to ground.    The fluorescence, from the higher $\pi\pi^*$ (singlet) level, is at about 660 m$\mu$.

In some cases the short-lived fluorescence is accompanied by a long-lived emission having the same spectrum.    This kind of emission signals a delayed return from the lowest excited singlet state to ground.    A mechanism for delayed emission is shown in Figure 7.12.    A metastable state (not necessarily a triplet) is populated by way of the first excited singlet; it is vacated by the same route.    If a direct transition from the metastable state to the ground state is impossible the excitation will be held in the metastable state until the system can absorb a quantum of energy sufficient to restore it to the excited singlet state.    After this delay the molecule can return to its ground state, emitting a quantum of light as it does so.    The energy needed for the transition from the metastable state to the excited singlet is gained through collisional interactions, and thus the depopulation of the metastable state is accelerated by heating.    The dependence of emission intensity on temperature is known as a glow curve; it gives information on the energy gap between the metastable state (or states) and the fluorescent singlet state.

Delayed light emission by Chl and BChl in living photosynthetic tissues was discovered by B. L. Strehler and W. Arnold.    The glow curves indicated that many metastable states of different depths are involved. The metastable states apparently correspond to the trapping of excited electrons in a lattice of Chl molecules (see Chapter 12).

Another kind of delayed fluorescence has been observed recently in organic crystals.    A population of triplet states is first generated; these interact to annihilate one another.    Two triplet molecules are converted to one molecule in the ground state and one in the excited singlet state. The excited singlet molecule emits fluorescence as it returns to the ground state.

# 8. Spectroscopy and Photochemistry of Unimolecular Chlorophylls

## 8.1  Optical Properties of Chlorophylls

THE ABSORPTION spectra of chlorophylls (see Appendix I) and related molecules (for example, porphyrins) have been given extensive quantitative interpretations by J. R. Platt, W. T. Simpson, H. Kuhn, and others. The conclusions of these investigators are fairly consistent and plausible, and the quantitative agreement with the extremely complicated theory of molecular spectra is reassuring.

The main absorption bands of Chl and BChl are the Soret bands, in the region 350–450 m$\mu$, and the long wave bands in the red and near infrared regions of the spectrum.  These bands undoubtedly correspond to singlet $\pi\pi^*$ transitions because they are so intense.  Studies of dichroism (polarized absorption) have shown that the dipole moments of these transitions lie in the plane of the tetrapyrrole "head" of the Chl molecule.  The hydrocarbon (phytyl) "tail" attached to the molecule contributes nothing to the visible absorption spectrum.

The Soret and long wave bands are interpreted in terms of the coupling of the orbital magnetic moments of the excited electron and its unexcited partner.  The lowest $\pi\pi^*$ excitation involves a change in the orbital quantum number $\lambda$ from 4 to 5.  The moments of the excited ($\lambda = 5$) and the unexcited ($\lambda = 4$) electron can then be parallel ($5 + 4 = 9$) or antiparallel ($5 - 4 = 1$).  The former case yields the long wave band and the latter the Soret band.

It is observed further that the long wave bands are accompanied by lesser "satellite" bands.  The lesser bands are most pronounced and separated from the main bands in BChl, less so in Chl, and absent in protochlorophyll (the biosynthetic precursor of Chl).  This pattern can be correlated with the symmetry of the conjugated system of C and N atoms that carry the delocalized $\pi$ and $\pi^*$ electrons.  The system has roughly circular symmetry in protochlorophyll; it becomes progressively more elongated as one goes to Chl and then to BChl. Thus in BChl the $\pi$ orbital has distinct major and minor axes, and $\pi\pi^*$ transitions can be distinguished according to whether the dipole oscillation is parallel or perpendicular to the long axis. Such states would be degenerate in protochlorophyll and hence would be manifested as a single absorption band. The actual wavelengths and intensities of the major and satellite long wave bands (see Figure 8.1) are in reasonable agreement with the predictions of this model, the major band being identified with dipole oscillation perpendicular to the long axis. From measurements of the polarization of fluorescence Goedheer has shown that the dipole moments of the 575 m$\mu$ and 772 m$\mu$ transitions in BChl are mutually perpendicular, both lying in the molecular plane.

The Soret bands are also accompanied by satellites (see Figure 8.1), but the foregoing interpretation is less satisfactory for these bands. For one thing the Soret band in protochlorophyll is accompanied by a satellite. For another the satellite is on the long wave side of the main Soret band in BChl, whereas it is on the short wave side in Chl $a$ and protochlorophyll. The satellites of the Soret bands may represent vibrational sublevels rather than extra modes of dipole oscillation.

Measurements of the yield and lifetime of fluorescence and of the area under the long wave absorption band have been made for Chl in organic solvents, especially by R. Livingston, S. S. Brody, P. Latimer, O. Dmitrievsky and their collaborators. The data for Chl $a$, when extrapolated to infinite dilution (to eliminate errors arising from self-absorption of the fluorescence), are mutually consistent in terms of Equations [7.3.1]

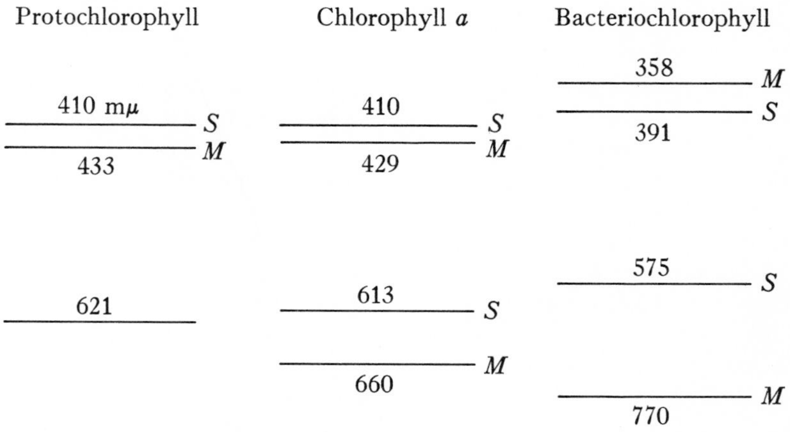

FIGURE 8.1. *Energy levels and corresponding wavelengths of main (M) and satellite (S) absorption bands of protochlorophyll, Chl a, and Bchl dissolved in ether.*

and [7.3.4]. Thus for Chl *a* in ether the natural lifetime of the lowest excited singlet state, computed from the long wave absorption band, is $15 \times 10^{-9}$ sec. The observed actual lifetime is $5 \times 10^{-9}$ sec, consistent with the observed quantum yield of 33%. For Chl *b* the actual lifetime is $3.5 \times 10^{-9}$ sec and the yield is 16%. These values predict a natural lifetime of $22 \times 10^{-9}$ sec, in reasonable agreement with the area under the absorption band. For Chl *a in vivo* the observations are not internally consistent; the situation appears to be complicated by the presence of fluorescent and nonfluorescent forms of Chl *a* (see Chapter 4). This problem will be examined in Chapter 13.

The occurrence of triplet excited states in Chl and the importance of these states in mediating photochemistry (see Section 8.2) has become well established, mainly through the studies pursued in the laboratories of R. Livingston, A. A. Krasnovskii, G. Porter, and H. Linschitz. A single flash of light, applied to a solution of Chl *a* in pyridine, can place more than 90% of the pigment in a metastable state of lifetime about $10^{-3}$ sec. The absorption spectrum of the metastable Chl *a* shows a broad band at 470 m$\mu$ and lesser bands extending toward the red. This spectrum is characteristic of the lowest $(\pi\pi^T)$ triplet state, the 470 m$\mu$ band corresponding to a transition to the next higher $\pi\pi^T$ state. The metastable state in Chl *a* is quenched efficiently by $O_2$, as would be expected. There is little doubt that it is the lowest $\pi\pi^T$ state. The decay of the triplet state in Chl follows complicated kinetics approximated by the expression

$$- \frac{dN_T}{dt} = k_1 N_T + k_2 N_T^2 + k_3 N_T N_G, \qquad [8.1.1]$$

where $N_T$ is the concentration of triplet-state molecules and $N_G$ is the concentration of ground-state molecules. The first term on the right can include the effects of external quenching substances, for which the contribution would be of the form $kN_T M$, where $M$ is the concentration of the quencher. The second term may then be regarded as a special case in which triplet Chl molecules are quenched by other triplet Chl molecules.

Further evidence for triplet states, both $n\pi^T$ and $\pi\pi^T$, is found in the phosphorescence of Chl. R. S. Becker and co-workers have observed that chlorophylls *a* and *b* in nonpolar solvents show characteristic spectra of phosphorescence at liquid nitrogen temperature. The wavelengths of the emission maxima are shown in Table 8.1. The fluorescence maxima in this table are for Chl in ether at room temperature; the phosphorescence maxima are for Chl in 3-methyl pentane. The two qualities of phosphorescence are ascribed logically to emission from the $n\pi^T$ and $\pi\pi^T$ triplet states, as indicated in the table. For either Chl *a* or *b* the longer wave phosphorescence was found to be about 50-fold less intense than the shorter wave phosphorescence. The fluorescence in dry hydrocarbon

TABLE 8.1.  Wavelengths of fluorescence and phosphorescence in Chl $a$ and Chl $b$, together with presumptive assignations of singlet and triplet excited states.  The measurements of phosphorescence were by R. S. Becker and collaborators.

|  | Chl a | Chl b |
|---|---|---|
| Fluorescence ($\pi\pi^*$) | 665 m$\mu$ | 649 |
| Phosphorescence ($n\pi^T$) | 755 | 733 |
| Phosphorescence ($\pi\pi^T$) | 885 | 875 |

solvent is weak or nonexistent, depending on the degree of dryness. The lifetimes of the phosphorescences were observed to be greater than $0.5 \times 10^{-3}$ sec.

It has been mentioned that transitions between singlet and triplet states are facilitated in the presence of heavy nuclei and paramagnetic substances.  In keeping with this expectation Becker found that replacement of the $Mg^{++}$ in Chl $b$ with $Cu^{++}$ caused an intensification of the long wave phosphorescence and a reduction of its lifetime.  In a similar vein it was shown that the Chl derivative pheophorbid $a$ shows fluorescence at 670 m$\mu$ and no phosphorescence, whereas Cu-substituted pheophorbid $a$ shows no fluorescence but emits short lived ($<10^{-4}$ sec) phosphorescence at 867 m$\mu$.

The implication of an $n\pi^T$ state in Chl $a$ and $b$ can be correlated with evidence for the $n\pi^*$ (singlet) state, but the entire body of evidence turns out to be somewhat contradictory.  The most suggestive fact is that Chl is fluorescent in polar solvents but not in nonpolar solvents such as thoroughly dried hydrocarbons.  A trace of water or ethanol, added to Chl in dry benzene, suffices to convert the Chl from a nonfluorescent to a fluorescent form.  This result has a rational explanation based on the relative energies of the lowest $n\pi^*$ and $\pi\pi^*$ states, as indicated in Figure 8.2.  If the $\pi\pi^*$ level is lower than the $n\pi^*$ level most of the excited molecules enter the $\pi\pi^*$ state before de-excitation.  Direct radiative return from the $\pi\pi^*$ level to ground can compete effectively with other pathways such as $\pi\pi^* \rightarrow \pi\pi^T \rightarrow$ ground, and fluorescence is accordingly seen.  But if the $n\pi^*$ level is the lower one it will provide a highly favored pathway for radiationless de-excitation $via$ the triplet states.

It is well established in simpler molecules that the relative positions of the lowest $n\pi^*$ and $\pi\pi^*$ levels can be inverted when a polar solvent is substituted for a nonpolar solvent, and that fluorescence does not occur when the $n\pi^*$ level lies below the $\pi\pi^*$ level.  The blue-shift (raising) of the $n\pi^*$ level in the presence of polar solvents has been attributed by M. Kasha to hydrogen bonding of the $n$ electrons to the solvent.  Because of this bonding the transition from $n$ to $\pi^*$ requires more energy.  But even if the foregoing explanation of Chl fluorescence is correct, the inversion of energy levels in Chl is probably not due to hydrogen bonding.  Livingston has

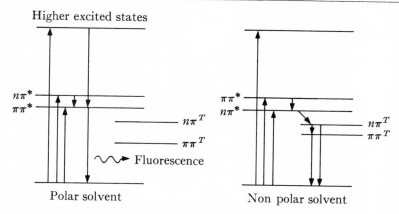

Higher excited states

Polar solvent

Non polar solvent

FIGURE 8.2.  *Hypothetical levels of excited states, and transitions corresponding to these states, for Chl dissolved in polar and nonpolar solvents.  Less probable transitions are omitted.*

found that the fluorescence of Chl in wet benzene involves a specific association between Chl and $H_2O$ molecules.  Chl forms addition compounds with generalized bases including ethanol and $H_2O$; the solvated compound is fluorescent.  This complexing requires the presence of the Mg atom.  It might be argued, then, that the $n$ electrons of the nitrogen atoms are involved in the lowest $n\pi^*$ transition, and that these electrons are bound more firmly by the central Mg atom when $H_2O$ is present as a complexant.  In that way the $n\pi^*$ level could become raised above the $\pi\pi^*$ level in the Chl·$H_2O$ complex.

Meanwhile osmometric determinations of the molecular weight of Chl in various solvents have shown that dimerization as well as complexing with bases determines the state and behavior of Chl *in vitro*.  In dry benzene, chloroform, or carbon tetrachloride Chl *a* exists as a nonfluorescent dimer; on the basis of infrared spectroscopy and analysis of nuclear magnetic resonance spectra the dimer link is between the Mg atom of one molecule and the carbonyl carbon atom in the cyclopentanone ring of the other. In "wet" solvents, such as chloroform containing ethanol, Chl *a* is monomeric and fluorescent.  Analysis of the optical properties of Chl *a* as functions of solvation, concentration and temperature have led Livingston to propose the following reactions:

$$\begin{aligned}
\text{base} + \text{dimer} &\rightleftharpoons \text{base·dimer} \\
\text{base} + \text{base·dimer} &\rightleftharpoons 2(\text{base·monomer}) \qquad [8.1.2]\\
\text{base} + \text{base·monomer} &\rightleftharpoons \text{dibase·monomer}
\end{aligned}$$

In these reactions monomer and dimer refer to Chl *a* and base refers to a generalized base such as ethanol.  The solvated monomeric species predominate in "wet" solvents.   All of the solvated forms, dimer and mono-mer alike, are fluorescent.

The absorption spectra of Chl $a$ and $b$ in dry and wet hydrocarbon solvents seem to provide additional evidence for the participation of $n\pi^*$ states.   It was observed by Livingston, by Freed and Sancier, and again by Becker that the main red ($\pi\pi^*$) band of Chl $a$ or $b$ exhibits a shoulder on its long wave side when the pigment is dissolved in a dry hydrocarbon. The shoulder disappears when a trace of ethanol is added to the solvent. It could be supposed that the shoulder reflects an $n\pi^*$ transition; blue-shift of this lesser band (attending the addition of ethanol) would cause it to merge with the larger $\pi\pi^*$ band.   The shoulder is more conspicuous in Chl $b$ than in Chl $a$; this could be correlated with the fact that Chl $b$ has one more —C═O residue, as a source of $n$ electrons, than Chl $a$.   But we have seen that an "$n\pi^*$" interpretation of the fluorescence behavior involves the $n$ electrons of the N atoms rather than the O atoms.

Another interpretation of the "long wave shoulder" in the spectrum of Chl in nonpolar solvents is that two species of Chl having different ground states are involved.   These could be two species of dimer, or even dimer and trimer, in view of the fact that Chl $b$ exists as a dimer in dry chloroform but as a trimer in dry carbon tetrachloride.   For Chl $b$ in dry hydrocarbon solvent the main red band is at 645 m$\mu$ and the shoulder is at 665 m$\mu$. The separation of these bands amounts to 0.06 ev.   A shoulder on the long wave side of the Soret band, distinct from the "usual" short wave satellite band, is also 0.06 ev from the main band.   This condition is consistent with the idea that two forms of Chl $b$ exist, with isoenergetic excited states but ground states that differ in energy by 0.06 ev.   The relative heights of the bands at 645 and 665 m$\mu$ vary with temperature in a way that suggests that the two forms are in equilibrium, and an Arrhenius plot of this temperature dependence yields an activation energy of 0.06 ev, in nice agreement with the energy gap as given by the absorption spectrum.

There are other complications in the use of $n\pi^*$ states to account for the optical properties of Chl.   Foremost is the fact that a $\pi\pi^* \leftrightarrow n\pi^*$ conversion should be forbidden.   The $\pi\pi^*$ transition dipole moment lies in the plane of the Chl molecule; the $n\pi^*$ moment is perpendicular to this plane.   This condition corresponds to zero dipole interaction between the two states.   But as with singlet-triplet transitions, many circumstances (such as collisions that disturb molecular symmetry) can facilitate the occurrence of "forbidden" events.

The explanation offered by Figure 8.2 for the fluorescence of Chl in wet and dry benzene is not consistent with observations of the yield of triplet Chl induced by illuminating the pigment in these solvents.   If the triplet states are fairly stable, the yield of triplet Chl should be considerably greater in dry benzene (where according to Figure 8.2 the $n\pi^*$ level is lower than the $\pi\pi^*$ level) than in wet benzene. This enhanced yield might not be observed if radiationless de-excitation from triplet to ground were especially efficient in dry benzene, but then the lifetime of the triplet state should be shorter in proportion to the lower observed yield. Actually the yield of triplet Chl in dry benzene is about one-fifth that in wet benzene, but the lifetime of the triplet state is no different in the two solvents. To retain the model of Figure 8.2 one must therefore make the additional assumption that the $n\pi^*$ state is degraded rapidly to the ground state by pathways that involve neither a conversion to the triplet state nor the emission of fluorescence.

Certainly the environment of Chl in benzene is simpler than that of Chl *in vivo*. Complexities are already abundant in the Chl-benzene system, and the behavior of Chl in living tissues can be expected to be far more complicated. Nevertheless the properties of Chl in wet and dry benzene are of considerable interest when it is recalled that Chl occurs *in vivo* in fluorescent and nonfluorescent forms, and that these forms may correspond to Chl in aqueous and lipid environments respectively.

## 8.2    Photochemistry of Chlorophyll *in vitro*

Five classes of photochemical reactions involving Chl have received considerable study in the hands of Livingston, Krasnovskii, Linschitz, G. Tollin, T. T. Bannister, H. Claes, L. P. Vernon, and others. These types of reactions are:

1. Photoreduction of Chl by certain electron donors.
2. Electron transfer from certain donors to certain acceptors, mediated by photo-excited Chl.
3. Chl-sensitized isomerization of poly-*cis* carotenoids.
4. Photo-oxidation of many substances, including Chl itself, with $O_2$ as the oxidant and Chl as the sensitizer.
5. Reversible light-induced bleaching of Chl in the presence of quinones, apparently due to electron transfer from Chl to quinone.

The first four types of reaction are probably mediated by Chl in its lowest excited triplet state ($Chl^T$). Considerations of photochemical yields and molecular collision frequencies show that these reactions involve Chl in a metastable state of duration of the order of milliseconds. We have seen that a triplet state of this lifetime is formed in Chl. Many of the photochemical reactants quench both the singlet and triplet excited states of Chl; complexes of the form ($Chl^T$):(Reactant) appear to be involved. G. Schenck has shown that in a variety of organic photo-oxidations a complex of triplet-state dye and $O_2$ is implicated as a reactive intermediate.

The five types of reactions listed above will now be described in more detail.

1. Ascorbate, sulfide, and phenylhydrazine can serve as electron donors for the photochemical reduction of Chl $a$ in polar solvents. These reactions are best observed in pyridine-water-alcohol mixtures, but the reaction with phenylhydrazine can also be observed in toluene. A specific role of water in the chemistry is suggested by the slower reaction rate observed (with ascorbate) when $D_2O$ is substituted for $H_2O$. The reduced Chl $a$ formed in these reactions is a pink substance with an absorption maximum at 523 m$\mu$. Analysis of the reaction mechanism is complicated by the formation of pheophytin and reduced pheophytin.

2. The same electron donors that afford photochemical reduction of Chl in aqueous pyridine can also lead to a Chl-sensitized reduction of other substances, notably azo dyes (such as methyl red), riboflavin, and $o$-dinitrobenzene. These reactions may be an extension of the photoreduction of Chl. There is some evidence, however, that the electron acceptor forms a complex with $Chl^T$ leading to oxidized Chl (and reduced acceptor) as a reaction intermediate. Thus methyl red is a strong quencher of Chl fluorescence but phenylhydrazine is not. Krasnovskii has shown that pyridine nucleotides can be reduced in this kind of reaction; such a reaction is of obvious interest in connection with photosynthesis.

A different reaction in this general category is the photochemical transfer of electrons between phenazine methosulfate (PMS) and various quinones. This kind of reaction, explored recently by L. P. Vernon, W. S. Zaugg, and E. Shaw, was found to be sensitized by Chl or BChl in aqueous media. The components were rendered water-soluble by adding detergents such as Triton X-100 or deoxycholate. Two ubiquinones, $UQ_2$ and $UQ_6$, and also trimethyl-1,4 benzoquinone (TMQ) were employed. Curiously enough the direction of the reaction was observed to depend on which quinone and which detergent was employed. With Triton and $UQ_2$ or $UQ_6$ the photochemical reaction was one in which reduced PMS became oxidized and the quinone became reduced. In the remaining cases (Triton and TMQ, or deoxycholate and any of the quinones) the light-driven reaction proceeded in the opposite direction. It has not been determined whether oxidized or reduced Chl is an intermediate in these reactions.

3. The photo-isomerization of carotenoids in the presence of Chl has been studied by H. Claes and T. O. M. Nakayama. Not only do carotenoids exhibit this reaction, they also interfere with the various photooxidations and reductions sensitized by Chl. The interference is pronounced if the carotenoid has a conjugated system containing nine or more double bonds; the efficacy with seven double bonds is marginal. Carotenoids are as effective as $O_2$ in quenching the triplet state of Chl.

The observations on isomerization and on interference with other reactions are consistent with the assumption that the carotenoids form complexes with $Chl^T$; the complex leads to de-excitation and in some cases to isomerization.   It is possible that a triplet level in the carotenoid, lying a little below that in Chl, acts as an energy sink, accepting the triplet energy from Chl and dissipating it into rotational and vibrational energy. On this basis one could argue that neurosporene, with nine conjugated double bonds, has a triplet level barely below that of Chl.   In less extensively conjugated polyenes (zeta-carotene, phytofluene, and phytoene) the triplet state is of higher energy than that in Chl and cannot act as an energy sink.

4. In contrast to photoreductions, the photo-oxidations sensitized by Chl (with $O_2$ as electron acceptor) are quite unspecific.   The oxidations occur in nonpolar as well as in polar solvents, and a wide range of substances including the Chl and the solvent can be oxidized.   The kinetics are in accord with the participation of $Chl^T \cdot O_2$ as a reactive intermediate.

5. Linschitz, and more recently G. Tollin and G. Green, have studied a photochemical reaction between Chl and quinone in EPA (ether-isopentane-alcohol) solvent.   The Chl is bleached reversibly upon illumination, and an ESR signal shows the formation of semi-reduced quinone $(Q^-)$.   No ESR signal corresponding to $Chl^+$ could be detected.   A $Chl \cdot Q$ complex and a polarized, excited $(Chl^+ \cdot Q^-)^*$ complex are implicated by the kinetics of formation and disappearance of the ESR signal at various temperatures.   Any similarity between this reaction and the ones involving PMS and quinones in aqueous media remains unknown.

Of the foregoing reaction types the first, second, and fifth may have a bearing on the mechanism of photosynthesis.   The third and fourth are related to the deleterious effects of photo-oxidations in plants, and to the ability of carotenoids to protect plants against these effects (see Chapter 13).

To some extent these studies of the photochemistry of Chl *in vitro* have been aimed at elucidating the mechanism of photosynthesis.   In this connection we seem to suffer from an embarrassment of wealth.   The presumably specific role of Chl in photosynthesis is not singled out from among the great variety of reactions catalyzed by Chl *in vitro*.

# 9. Some Consequences of Molecular Interactions

## 9.1  Introduction

SOME PROCESSES facilitated by mechanical interactions between molecules (collisions and lattice vibrations) have already been mentioned in Chapter 7.   Among these are the settling of ground and excited states into the lower vibrational levels, the processes of internal conversion and radiationless de-excitation, and the transitions between $n\pi^*$ and $\pi\pi^*$ states and between singlet and triplet states.

Aside from mechanical coupling two kinds of molecular interactions have major consequences for the behavior of a collection of molecules. The first of these is interaction through electric forces arising from the redistribution of charge in an electronic transition.   The electric dipole and multipole fields of one molecule induce excitation in another; in this way excitation energy can be propagated through an ensemble of molecules.   This phenomenon will be the subject of Section 9.2.

The remaining kind of molecular interaction that we shall consider is the overlap of electron orbitals from one molecule to another.   This interaction leads to a variety of effects characterized by the transfer or migration of electric charge.   The occurrence of charge displacement is facilitated both by field interactions and electron orbital overlap; these factors promote entry into bimolecular charge transfer states as well as into $n\pi^*$ and triplet states.   The potential importance of such states for the trapping of excitation energy in a collection of molecules will be discussed in Section 9.3.

Another consequence of electron orbital overlap is the electric conductivity that can arise in molecular aggregates as a result of photo-ionization.   This topic will be treated in Section 9.4.

## 9.2  Electric Dipole Interaction: Migration of Electronic Excitation Energy

Excitation energy can be transferred from one molecule (the sensitizer, denoted $S$) to another (the acceptor, $A$) by a coupled event in which de-excitation of $S$ is accompanied by a concomitant excitation of $A$. The mechanism can be likened to the transfer of energy between coupled pendulums or other oscillators. This process was recognized in atomic vapors by G. Cario and J. Franck in 1923. One can imagine that $S$ generates an electromagnetic field during its de-excitation, and $A$ is excited by this field rather than by an external electromagnetic field. This transfer event is in competition with other pathways of de-excitation of $S$, such as fluorescence. But the energy transfer mechanism is entirely distinct from the trivial process in which $S$ emits a fluorescent quantum that is reabsorbed by $A$. The time required for energy transfer can be much shorter than the fluorescence lifetime of $S$ and the efficiency of transfer can be much greater than the maximum observable efficiency of fluorescence of $S$.

Evidence for the transfer of excitation energy among dye molecules is found most strikingly in the phenomenon of sensitized fluorescence. Absorption of light by $S$ leads to fluorescence of $A$:

$$S + h\nu_a \rightarrow S^*,$$
$$S^* + A \rightarrow S + A^*, \qquad [9.2.1]$$
$$A^* \rightarrow A + h\nu_f,$$

where $h\nu_a$ and $h\nu_f$ are absorbed and fluorescent light quanta. Energy transfer among dye molecules in solution has been recorded many times; efficient transfer can occur over distances as great as 100 Å. In photosynthetic tissues a transfer of energy from accessory pigments to Chl has been demonstrated by R. Emerson and C. M. Lewis, W. Arnold and J. R. Oppenheimer, A. J. Dutton and W. M. Manning, and many others. In these observations the criteria included sensitization of photosynthesis as well as of fluorescence. Bannister has shown that a dye complexed to a protein molecule receives excitation energy absorbed by the protein. In polymers such as nucleic acids, reactions in one part of the molecule effected by light absorbed in another part are best explained on the basis of excitation energy transfer.

Sensitized phosphorescence has been observed by A. N. Terenin and V. L. Ermolaev, indicating that energy can be transferred by way of triplet as well as singlet states. These experiments were designed to eliminate the possibility that energy transfer *via* singlet states was followed by singlet $\rightarrow$ triplet conversion in the acceptor. Recent elaborations of such experiments, performed with crystals of naphthalene and anthracene containing traces of other substances, have shown not only the occurrence of energy transfer *via* triplet states but also the interaction between two triplet excitations to produce a higher excited state.

In a set of molecules of the same kind it is impossible to detect sensitized fluorescence because sensitizer and acceptor cannot be distinguished. A different kind of evidence for energy transfer is then useful; namely, the phenomenon of "concentration-depolarization" of fluorescence. If polarized light is absorbed by a set of molecules that are neither rotating nor transferring energy among each other, the light emitted as fluorescence will also be polarized. If the molecules can rotate (as a result of Brownian motion) during the excitation lifetime, the polarization of the fluorescence will become lost, that is, randomized. The polarization of fluorescence will also become lost if the energy is transferred among randomly oriented molecules before it is emitted. Thus in situations that exclude rapid Brownian motion (for example, in sufficiently viscous or rigid media) the depolarization of fluorescence implies energy transfer. The effect is greater in more concentrated dye solutions because the energy transfer becomes more efficient as the molecules are crowded closer together.

We have been speaking as if the excitation energy could be conceived as being localized in one molecule and then transferred to another. However, if the electric field interactions between molecules are strong it is necessary to describe energy transfer by a "delocalized" formulation in which the excitation energy is treated as a property of the whole ensemble. With weaker field interaction (the criterion will be given presently) a "localized" treatment is still formally incorrect but gives a satisfactory approximation when used properly. The conditions affording a localized description are probably met in a biological molecular aggregate such as the photosynthetic unit.

In a delocalized treatment the excitation is regarded as belonging to the collection of molecules as a whole, and wave functions describing the entire system in its excited and ground states are constructed. The wave functions are obtained as solutions of the Schrödinger equation:

$$H\Psi = -\frac{ih}{2\pi}\frac{\partial\Psi}{\partial t} \qquad [9.2.2]$$

for time-varying states and

$$H\Psi_j = E_j\Psi_j \qquad [9.2.3]$$

for stationary states. In these equations $E_j$ is the total energy of the system in the $j$th stationary state and $H$ is the quantum-mechanical operator (the Hamiltonian) that corresponds to energy. $H$ is made up of two terms, one representing the energies of the molecules in isolation and the other the energy of interaction between the molecules. The optical properties of the ensemble (absorption and emission spectra and characteristics of energy transfer) can be deduced from the wave functions and the eigenvalues for total energy and interaction energy.

Solutions to this problem are feasible only when the interaction energy is simplified by ignoring some contributions and taking average values for others.   One simplification, followed in Kasha's "molecular exciton" treatment, is to ignore any contribution due to intermolecular overlap of electron orbitals.   Another is to retain only the electric dipole portion of the radiative interaction.   In this simplification the redistribution of charge that accompanies a transition is described and the corresponding electric potential function is written as a function of the spatial coordinates.   The part of this potential function that pertains to electric dipoles carries an inverse third power dependence on distance.   It is the predominant term in the function in the case of strongly allowed transitions; the other (higher multipole) terms can then be ignored.

A final simplification concerns the vibrational interactions and takes different forms that will be described for two extreme cases.   In a localized description one speaks of the time of residence of the excitation in any one molecule;† this is also called the transfer time $\tau_t$ and is the reciprocal of the rate of transfer $n_t$.   If $\tau_t$ is greater than the period of collisional or lattice vibrations (about $3 \times 10^{-12}$ sec in a condensed phase) the excited molecules will, during their individual excitation lifetimes, enter a distribution among vibrational states as dictated by thermal equilibrium. This condition usually affords a satisfactory use of the localized treatment. At the other extreme is the case in which the transfer time is less than the period of nuclear oscillations (about $3 \times 10^{-14}$ sec) as well as collisional or lattice vibrations.   A localized treatment is then unsatisfactory, but the "localized" language can be helpful in discussing the relationships between electronic excitation and vibrations in the system.   At this extreme the nuclear parameters of a molecule do not change appreciably during the time $(\tau_t)$ that the molecule carries a quantum of excitation.   The effects of vibrations on the transfer rate can therefore be ignored.   Between the foregoing extremes is a third case where $\tau_t$ lies between about $3 \times 10^{-14}$ and $3 \times 10^{-12}$ sec (greater than the period of intramolecular nuclear oscillations, but less than the period of collisional or lattice vibrations). The properties of energy transfer in this case are different from those in the two other cases.

The three aforementioned situations were distinguished by Franck and E. Teller in 1938.   The case of slow transfer, amenable to a localized treatment, has been developed by F. Perrin and T. Förster under the name "resonance transfer."   Perrin's earliest treatment of the problem was in

† One must distinguish between the duration of residence of the excitation in one molecule and the lifetime of excitation in the entire ensemble.   The latter corresponds to the observed lifetime of fluorescence.   If the sole effect of molecular interactions is to afford energy transfer, the excitation lifetime in the ensemble is the same as that which would be observed in one isolated molecule.   The probability of fluorescent de-excitation is then independent of which molecule is carrying the excitation; the lifetime is not "renewed" after each transfer.   These remarks must be qualified by the possibility that under very strong interactions the emission probability may be altered somewhat.   However, this qualification should not apply to Chl *in vivo*.

terms of classical physics and described the resonant coupling of two oscillating electric dipoles of the same frequency. The reformulation in terms of quantum theory was begun by Perrin and perfected by Förster. The other cases ($\tau_t < 10^{-12}$ sec) have been described in the "molecular exciton" theory of A. S. Davydov and its elaboration by W. T. Simpson and D. L. Peterson, M. Kasha, and others.

Förster has recently designated the three cases as "fast," "intermediate," and "slow" transfer. The distinction as made in terms of $\tau_t$ can be recast in terms of certain energy values of the system; it is then easier to avoid the language of localization. Characteristic times and energies are related roughly as follows. The period of nuclear oscillation, about $3 \times 10^{-14}$ sec, corresponds to a spacing, $\Delta\epsilon$ (expressed in wave number) of about 1000 $cm^{-1}$ between successive vibrational levels. A $3 \times 10^{-12}$ sec period for collisional or lattice vibrations imparts a width, $\Delta\epsilon'$, of about 10 $cm^{-1}$ to each vibrational level (the broadening due to rotations is usually less for large molecules). The transfer time is correlated with the dipole interaction energy $\epsilon$, strong interaction leading to a short transfer time. The three cases of energy transfer are then distinguished according to the criteria

$$\text{Fast, } \epsilon > \Delta\epsilon$$
$$\text{Intermediate, } \Delta\epsilon > \epsilon > \Delta\epsilon' \qquad [9.2.4]$$
$$\text{Slow, } \Delta\epsilon' > \epsilon.$$

Some properties of these three cases will now be described.

In fast transfer the relatively slow vibrations do not come into play, and the dipole resonance is between identical electronic states of the interacting molecules. The transfer rate is independent of temperature and of wavelength of the exciting light; it is directly proportional to the interaction energy, and hence varies inversely as the third power of the distance between molecules in the case of dipole interaction.

In intermediate transfer the resonance is among vibrational levels in the interacting molecules, as sketched on a localized basis in Figure 9.1. The probability of transfer depends therefore on the way that the ground and excited state vibrational levels are populated. An allowed de-excitation in the sensitizer molecule must terminate at a vibrational level that is occupied in the acceptor molecule. Consequently, the transfer rate varies slightly with exciting wavelength, which determines the vibrational level occupied in the excited state, and with temperature, which determines the levels in the ground state that can mediate transfer. The temperature dependence is predicted to be negligible except at very low temperatures such that the ground state molecules are all in the lowest vibrational level. The rate of transfer is again proportional to $\epsilon$ and hence to $R^{-3}$ (where $R$ is the intermolecular distance) for dipole interaction.

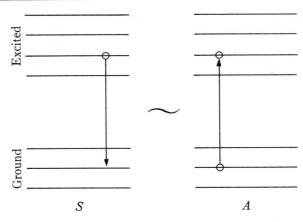

FIGURE 9.1.   *Details of electronic transitions in sensitizer and acceptor showing the involvement of vibrational states during energy transfer of the "intermediate" kind, according to a "localized" description.*

In the case of slow transfer the excitation can be imagined to reside in one molecule for a time sufficient to allow thermal equilibration among the vibrational levels.   The excited molecules will settle into the lower vibrational levels before transferring their energy, and the amount of energy transferred corresponds to a transition from one of these lower levels to the ground state.   The same amount of energy must be gained by the acceptors in the transfer process.   These events are illustrated in Figure 9.2 for the case of dissimilar sensitizer ($S$) and acceptor ($A$) mole-

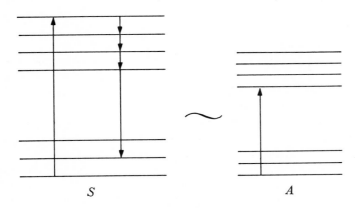

FIGURE 9.2.   *The same as Figure 9.1 but for "slow" transfer.   The energy lost in the final de-excitation of S equals that gained by A.   If A were absent, the same sequence of events in S would result in its fluorescence.*

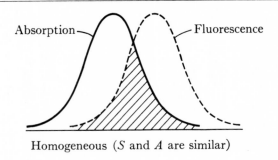

Homogeneous (*S* and *A* are similar)

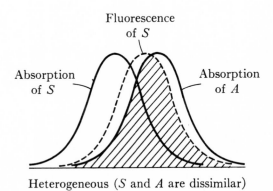

Heterogeneous (*S* and *A* are dissimilar)

FIGURE 9.3. *Overlap between the fluorescence band of a sensitizer and the absorption band of an acceptor, upon which the efficiency of "slow" energy transfer depends. The overlap is shown by the shaded area. It can be greater when sensitizer and acceptor are dissimilar (lower curves) than when they are similar (upper curves).*

cules. The pathway of de-excitation in *S* is like that followed in fluorescence of *S*. Consequently, the probability (or rate) of transfer is proportional to the amount of overlap between the fluorescence spectrum of *S* and the absorption spectrum of *A*. The overlap, and hence the transfer rate, is maximal when *S* and *A* are dissimilar and the absorption band of *A* is at slightly greater wavelengths than that of *S* (see Figure 9.3). Thus we are led to the interesting result that heterogeneous transfer can be more efficient than homogeneous transfer in the "slow" case. The rate of slow transfer is independent of exciting wavelength because thermal relaxation brings *S* to a lower vibrational level in the excited state, regardless of which higher level had been entered in the absorption process. The transfer rate depends on temperature to the extent that the overlap between fluorescence and absorption bands is affected; this temperature dependence should be greater than that expected in intermediate transfer.

TABLE 9.1. Characteristics of the intermolecular transfer of electronic excitation energy as described by Förster. The mean pairwise transfer time is $\tau_t$; it must be small compared with the singlet excitation lifetime for efficient transfer to occur. The dipole interaction energy is $\epsilon$. $C$ is the concentration of a solution of pigment molecules giving the corresponding mean values of $\tau_t$ and $\epsilon$ for strongly allowed dipole transitions. $R$ is the corresponding mean intermolecular distance.

| Transfer mechanism | Description | Approximate range of applicability | | | | Dependence of transfer rate on intermolecular distance, exciting wavelength, and temperature | | |
| --- | --- | --- | --- | --- | --- | --- | --- | --- |
| | | $\tau$, sec | $\epsilon$, cm$^{-1}$ | $C$, $M$ | $R$, Å | $R$ | $\lambda$ | $T$ |
| fast | delocalized ("molecular exciton") | $<3 \times 10^{-14}$ | $>1000$ | $>5$ | $<5$ | $R^{-3}$ | | |
| intermediate | delocalized ("molecular exciton") | $3 \times 10^{-14}$–$3 \times 10^{-12}$ | $10$–$1000$ | $0.1$–$5$ | $5$–$20$ | $R^{-3}$ | slight | slight |
| slow | localized ("resonance transfer") | $3 \times 10^{-12}$–$3 \times 10^{-8}$ | $0.1$–$10$ | $3 \times 10^{-4}$–$0.1$ | $20$–$100$ | $R^{-6}$ | | moderate |

The rate of slow transfer is proportional to the square of the interaction energy and hence varies as $R^{-6}$, rather than $R^{-3}$, for dipole interaction.

Properties of fast, intermediate, and slow transfer are summarized in Table 9.1. The figures for concentration and intermolecular separation were taken from calculations by Förster.

Experimental discrimination between the three types of energy transfer is difficult and can be complicated by a mixing of types; clusters of strongly interacting molecules may interact weakly to form larger aggregates, with faster transfer within the clusters and slower transfer between them. This situation can arise in solutions of polymers and in crystals having two or more molecules per unit cell.

The type of transfer that can occur is usually predicted from estimates of the interaction energy. These estimates are commonly based on absorption spectra of the pigment in the aggregate, as compared with spectra of widely separated pigment molecules (as in dilute solution). The weak interaction leading to slow transfer should have no discernible effect on the absorption spectrum. Under intermediate transfer the spectrum should differ slightly from the unimolecular form, and in the case of fast transfer the spectrum should be altered radically because the vibrational structure is suppressed.

Unfortunately, the absorption spectra of molecules in an aggregate are sensitive to many factors; it is often difficult to abstract and evaluate the contributions of electric dipole and multipole interactions. In the case of fast transfer the vibrational splitting is lost but the "exciton splitting" (see later in this section) takes its place. We shall see that the effects of exciton splitting can take a variety of forms (Figure 9.6).

In aggregates having an ordered structure the dipole interaction cannot be estimated simply from the intermolecular distance because the dipole coupling between two molecules depends on the relative orientations of the transition dipole moments. This parameter enters in the manner shown in Figure 9.4. The transfer rate between two molecules is proportional to

$$(\cos \phi_{SA} - 3 \cos \phi_S \cos \phi_A)^2; \qquad [9.2.5]$$

for random orientation this factor has a mean value of $\frac{2}{3}$. If the transition dipole moments of two molecules are mutually perpendicular and one of them lies on the line connecting the molecules, the interaction is zero. An ensemble can therefore be arranged so that all of the nearest-neighbor interactions are zero. Meanwhile the electron orbitals could overlap and cause a profound change in the absorption spectrum accompanied by very little dipole interaction.

A shift in the excited energy level, occasioned by some sort of molecular interaction (for example, electron orbital overlap), could show a statistical

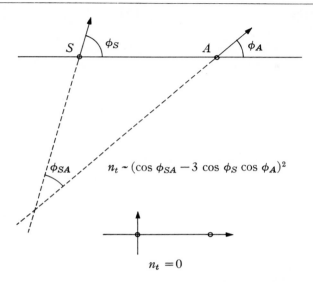

FIGURE 9.4.    *Dependence of the rate $n_t$ of energy transfer between two molecules upon the orientations of their transition dipole moments.   The moments make angles $\phi_S$ and $\phi_A$ with a line connecting the molecules and $\phi_{SA}$ with each other.*

distribution of its magnitude in an aggregate of molecules.   The absorption band would then be broadened in a way that could be mistaken for vibrational broadening or exciton splitting.   This broadening might or might not vary with temperature and other factors; it would certainly confuse the evaluation of the effects of dipole interaction.   As a single example, suppose that an absorption band is shifted toward greater wavelengths as a result of intermolecular binding and is broadened because the binding forces have a statistical distribution.   The long wave side of the band then reflects regions in the aggregate where the binding is stronger, and the short wave side reflects regions where it is weaker.   The efficiency of slow transfer may then be greater when light is absorbed in the long wave part of the band.   This dependence on exciting wavelength could be taken incorrectly as evidence for intermediate transfer.

In spite of these difficulties one can often make reasonable judgments regarding the type of transfer that is possible.   The fast and intermediate mechanisms are possible in molecular crystals and in polymers made from identical monomers.   In biological aggregates such as photosynthetic units the interaction energy is probably about 30 cm$^{-1}$, near the borderline between intermediate and slow transfer.

We shall turn now to a brief examination of the molecular exciton model as developed by Kasha and collaborators to describe energy transfer in polymers. This delocalized treatment does not apply to slow transfer, as vibrational interactions are ignored. Consider a dimer made up of molecules $Q_1$ and $Q_2$. Whereas the localized picture deals with excited states $Q_1{}^* + Q_2$ and $Q_1 + Q_2{}^*$, the delocalized treatment involves a ground state $(Q_1 \cdot Q_2)$ and an excited state $(Q_1 \cdot Q_2)^*$ that is split into two levels. The wave functions for the two localized conditions $(Q_1{}^* + Q_2$ and $Q_1 + Q_2{}^*)$ are $\Psi_1{}^*\Psi_2$ and $\Psi_1\Psi_2{}^*$. Linear combinations of these yield appropriate wave functions for the two levels of $(Q_1 \cdot Q_2)^*$:

$$\Psi = \frac{1}{\sqrt{2}} (\Psi_1{}^*\Psi_2 \pm \Psi_1\Psi_2{}^*). \qquad [9.2.6]$$

This is illustrated in Figure 9.5 for a dimer whose transition dipole moments† are perpendicular to an axis through the center of each dipole. The positive sign in Equation [9.2.6] is for the upper (antibonding) state in which the transition dipoles of the individual molecules are parallel (that is, in phase). The energy gap between the two levels is twice the dipole interaction energy.

In this example a transition from the ground state to the upper state is allowed and to the lower state forbidden. This can be seen from a qualitative argument: The dimer is much smaller than the wavelength of the exciting light, so both molecules will be in the same small region of the radiation field. The phase of the electromagnetic wave will be the same throughout this region, and so the transition dipoles generated by the radiation field ought to be in phase with each other. If the transition dipoles are aligned with the dimer axis the allowed configuration $(\rightarrow \rightarrow)$ is attractive and the forbidden one $(\rightarrow \leftarrow)$ repulsive; in that case a transition to the lower of the two excited states is allowed. In an oblique arrangement, $\nearrow \searrow$ and $\nearrow \nwarrow$, both configurations have "in-phase" components and transitions to both states are allowed. When this approach is extended to $N$ coupled molecules, $N$ excited states are generated through linear combinations of wave functions such as $\Psi_1\Psi_2 \ldots \Psi_s{}^* \ldots \Psi_N$. One can expect various situations (see Figure 9.6), depending on the symmetry of the array. In this figure allowed transitions are shown by solid lines and forbidden ones by dashed lines. It can be seen that all kinds of spectral manifestations are predicted: blue-shift, red-shift, no shift, narrow or broad bands, band splitting, et cetera. In example (a) a special case arises when $\alpha = \cos^{-1} (1/\sqrt{3})$: the interaction energy is then zero and no splitting occurs. Band splitting in Chl dimers has been studied by Brody; the single maximum at 665 m$\mu$ is split into two at 648 and 682 m$\mu$.

---

† Although the excitation is treated as belonging to the dimer as a whole, it remains helpful to visualize a quantum of excitation (an exciton) oscillating between the two monomers.

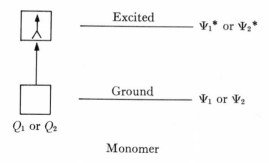

Monomer

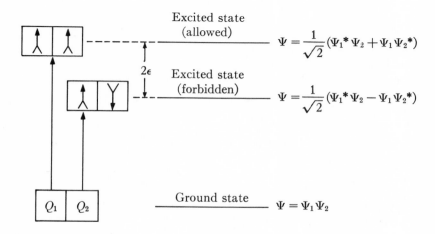

Dimer

FIGURE 9.5.   *Energy levels and corresponding wave functions in a dimer consisting of two identical molecules $Q_1$ and $Q_2$. The transition dipole moments are shown by small arrows within the boxes representing the molecules. The dipole interaction energy is $\epsilon$.*

In Figure 9.6(a) a triplet level is drawn between the top and bottom of the set of singlet levels for a linear polymer with parallel dipole moments. Here a change in structure from $\alpha > \cos^{-1}(1/\sqrt{3})$ to $\alpha < \cos^{-1}(1/\sqrt{3})$ could cause an overwhelming change in the population of the triplet state. In the case $\alpha > \cos^{-1}(1/\sqrt{3})$ the forbidden levels are inaccessible from the ground state but can be entered from the highest (allowed) level. This kind of polymer may therefore be nonfluorescent, in contrast to the one for which $\alpha < \cos^{-1}(1/\sqrt{3})$.   In Figure 9.6(d) a triplet state could be populated efficiently if it lay near the bottom of the exciton band.

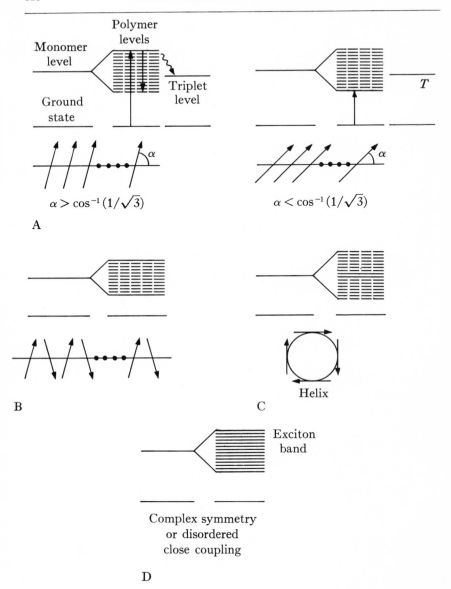

FIGURE 9.6. *Multiple energy levels (exciton levels) in various polymers. The alignments of dipole moments are shown by arrows. Levels corresponding to forbidden transitions from the ground state are shown by dashed lines; allowed levels by solid lines. In case (a), a linear polymer with parallel dipole moments, the angle $\alpha$ between the dipole moments and the polymer axis determines whether the uppermost or the lowest excited level is allowed.*

Until recently the possibility of energy migration *via* triplet states in molecular aggregates received little attention.    The long life of the triplet state was felt to be more than offset by the weakness of the molecular interactions (electron exchange resonance energies) that could lead to energy migration.    At this writing, thanks to the work of G. W. Robinson, S. P. McGlynn, D. S. McClure, and many others, the triplet state has emerged as an important carrier of excitation energy in molecular crystals. New experiments, made feasible in part by laser excitation and supported by new theoretical justifications, have shown that triplet exciton migration can actually be more extensive than singlet migration in crystals of aromatic compounds.    From an analysis of phosphorescence band shifts in benzene crystals Robinson has adduced a transfer rate of $10^{12}$ per sec for triplet excitation.    Extensive triplet migration in naphthalene and anthracene has been indicated by the efficiencies of biphotonic processes, in which two triplet excitons interact to produce one excitation quantum of greater energy.    An example is the blue fluorescence elicited in anthracene by red exciting light.    The red light excites only the lowest triplet state, as shown by the fact that the excitation spectrum for blue fluorescence corresponds to the spectrum of red phosphorescence.    Two triplet excitons then interact to excite the fluorescent singlet state.    This biphotonic mechanism is confirmed by the fact that the intensity of the fluorescence is proportional to the square of the exciting light intensity.

It is too early to assess the impact of these findings in the field of photosynthesis.    To date there is no evidence for the importance of triplet exciton migration in the operation of a photosynthetic unit (see Sections 12.3 and 13.2).

### 9.3    Polarized States and Energy Sinks

In studying the operation of a photosynthetic unit we shall have to consider not only the transfer of excitation energy but also the trapping of the energy at a reaction center and the consequent mediation of photochemistry.

Energy trapping requires that the excitation becomes fixed in one molecule (or molecular complex) through entry into a localized excited state. Two examples can be listed for the case of slow transfer in a localized description; they are illustrated in Figure 9.7a and b.    In the first case a trapping molecule ($Q_T$ in the Figure) is an energy sink because its singlet excited level is lower than that of the transferring molecules $Q$.    Resonance transfer from $Q$ to $Q_T$ is irreversible because of this difference in energy; thus, the excitation becomes trapped as singlet excitation energy in $Q_T$. The overlap between the fluorescence spectrum of $Q$ and the absorption spectrum of $Q_T$ will be greater than the fluorescence-absorption overlap

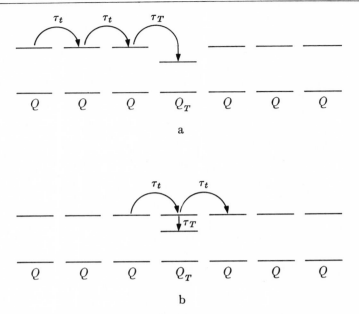

FIGURE 9.7. *Two mechanisms for the trapping of excitation energy at a molecule $Q_T$ in an ensemble of "transferring" molecules $Q$. In case (a) the excited singlet level of $Q_T$ lies below that of $Q$; in (b) there is a state just below the excited singlet state in $Q_T$ but not in $Q$. Efficient trapping will occur if the trapping time $\tau_T$ is less than the transfer time $\tau_t$.*

for two similar molecules $Q$ (see Figure 9.3). The "trapping time" $\tau_T$, which in this case is the "$Q \to Q_T$" transfer time, is therefore less than $\tau_t$, the "$Q \to Q$" transfer time, other factors remaining equal. Accordingly, the probability of trapping is at least as high as the chance that the excitation quantum will encounter $Q_T$ during its migration. In the second case (Figure 9.6b) the singlet level of $Q_T$ is not depressed but another excited state of lower energy, peculiar to $Q_T$, can be entered *via* the singlet state. The fate of a quantum in the singlet state of $Q_T$ (trapping *vs.* continued migration) is determined by the ratio of trapping time $\tau_T$ to transferring time $\tau_t$. Efficient trapping can occur only if $\tau_T << \tau_t$. The lower state in $Q_T$, missing or not participating in $Q$, could be (among other things) an $n\pi^*$ state, a triplet state, or a charge transfer state.

In these descriptions $\tau_t$ is not the same as $\tau_p$, the simple pairwise transfer time for two isolated molecules as calculated from Förster's theory. It is less by a factor $B$ equal to the number of nearest neighbors of any one molecule:

$$\tau_t = \tau_p/B. \qquad [9.3.1]$$

This change must be made if the localized treatment is to give a correct prediction in correspondence with the (rigorously correct) delocalized treatment. In effect we must recognize that the rate of transfer to one neighbor is increased by the presence of the others. In classical terms the resonances of the several nearest neighbors reinforce each other.

We may now say that the mean total time needed for the migration and trapping of a quantum, written $\langle \tau \rangle$, is equal to $\tau_t$ multiplied by the mean number of "$Q \rightarrow Q$" transfers required for the quantum to encounter $Q_T$ (this will be so if $\tau_T < < \tau_t$). The outcome for a three-dimensional aggregate, with six nearest neighbors to any one molecule, is

$$\langle \tau \rangle = 0.4N^{2/3}\tau_p = 2.4N^{2/3}\tau_t, \qquad [9.3.2]$$

where $N$ is the number of interacting molecules. For a two-dimensional aggregate with four nearest neighbors the result is

$$\langle \tau \rangle = \frac{1}{4}(1.3N - N^{1/2})\tau_p = (1.3N - N^{1/2})\tau_t. \qquad [9.3.3]$$

Because of the inverse sixth power dependence on molecular separation in slow transfer, the contribution of non-nearest-neighbor jumps is relatively small and can be ignored.†

Some numerical consequences of Equations [9.3.2] and [9.3.3] are of interest. If $N = 300$ in a three-dimensional aggregate and $\tau_t = 10^{-12}$ sec, which is near the limiting value for slow transfer, $\langle \tau \rangle$ is about $10^{-10}$ sec according to [9.3.2] and about $4 \times 10^{-10}$ sec according to [9.3.3]. If the natural lifetime of excitation $\tau_0$ is $10^{-8}$ sec, a value of $10^{-10}$ sec for $\langle \tau \rangle$ gives a trapping efficiency of 99%, provided that fluorescence and trapping are the only avenues of de-excitation. These values are within reason for a photosynthetic unit; we shall return to this point more critically in Chapter 12.

An entirely different situation can be visualized, in which the trapping time $\tau_T$ is much greater than the time required for the excitation to reach the neighborhood of the trap. In that case the excitation visits all parts of the ensemble with equal probability before being trapped; in localized terms each molecule has a probability $1/N$ of carrying the excitation at any instant. The total time $\langle \tau \rangle$ between excitation and trapping is then equal to $N \cdot \tau_T$. In contrast to the previous case, $\langle \tau \rangle$ is independent of the dimensionality of the system and of the pairwise transfer time. Instead it depends on the trapping time $\tau_T$. For this case, with $\langle \tau \rangle$ equal to $10^{-10}$ sec and $N = 300$, $\tau_T = 3 \times 10^{-13}$ sec and $\tau_t$ is less than $\tau_T$. Such strong coupling probably does not occur in photosynthetic tissues.

† The considerations of the last two paragraphs have been developed recently by Z. Bay and R. M. Pearlstein. Earlier calculations, based strictly on a localized treatment with pairwise interactions, predicted erroneously large values of $\langle \tau \rangle$.

If the trapped state is nonfluorescent the yield of fluorescence in the ensemble cannot be greater than $\langle\tau\rangle/\tau_0$. Thus the quenching of fluorescence in molecular aggregates is often taken as evidence for energy transfer into trapping centers. However, this is by no means the only possible explanation of quenching in molecular aggregates. The quenching of fluorescence could, for example, be due to wholesale singlet $\rightarrow$ triplet conversion engendered by the aggregation. In any case artificial aggregates of Chl have been shown to be nonfluorescent.

The existence of traps could be based on a variety of effects. An energy level in the trapping molecule could be depressed, forming an energy sink, as a result of special environmental influences. Thus an $n\pi^*$ level might be lowered by a local electric attraction that encourages the charge displacement involved in the transition. A $\pi\pi^*$ level might be lowered through distortion of the $\pi$ and $\pi^*$ orbitals, occasioned either by local electric fields or through electron orbital overlap. A slight specialization in the structure of the trapping molecule could also lower these levels.

A trapping center is automatically a point of asymmetry in an ensemble of "transferring" molecules; the spoiling of symmetry in the neighborhood of the trap could facilitate forbidden transitions such as the entry into a triplet state.

A specific complexing of the trapping molecule with another molecule $(Q_T \cdot M)$, with considerable overlap in the excited state orbitals of the two, can engender a bimolecular charge transfer state: an excited state in which the complex is polarized $(Q_T^+ \cdot M^-$ or $Q_T^- \cdot M^+)$. A state of this kind is especially interesting for the mechanism of photosynthesis. In addition to its potentiality as a trap for excitation energy, a charge transfer state shows the beginnings of a separation of oxidizing and reducing power.

The theory and description of bimolecular charge transfer states has been elaborated mainly by R. S. Mulliken. Such states can be visualized as intermolecular analogues of highly polarized excited states in single molecules. Many organic molecules exist in what can be described as a state of resonance between unpolarized and polarized configurations. The actual wave functions for such molecules can be constructed by superimposing idealized wave functions $\Psi_I$ and $\Psi_{II}$ that correspond to the idealized (unpolarized and polarized) configurations, as indicated in Figure 9.8. In the actual ground state the unpolarized configuration is dominant; the actual excited state is mainly polarized. The ground state energy is less than that of the fictitious unpolarized state; this stabilization of the ground state can be attributed to resonance between the two idealized configurations. This description can be extended to a bimolecular complex in which one molecule $(D)$ acts as an electron donor and the other $(A)$ as an acceptor. The polarized idealized configuration (wave function $\Psi_{II}$) is one in which an electron has been transferred from $D$ to $A$.

Two idealized configurations of an organic molecule:

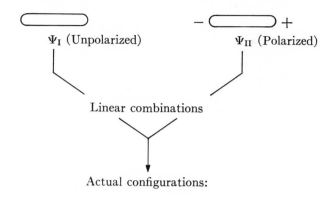

$\Psi_I$ (Unpolarized)            $\Psi_{II}$ (Polarized)

Linear combinations

Actual configurations:

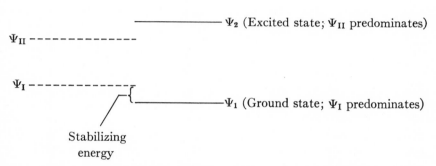

$\Psi_{II}$ - - - - - - - - - - - - -          ——————— $\Psi_2$ (Excited state; $\Psi_{II}$ predominates)

$\Psi_I$ - - - - - - - - - - - - -          $\Psi_1$ (Ground state; $\Psi_I$ predominates)

Stabilizing
energy

FIGURE 9.8.   *Construction of actual ground state and excited state wave functions for a molecule by superimposing the wave functions for idealized configurations (see text).*

The actual ground and excited states of the complex are hybrids of the "pure $D \cdot A$" and "pure $D^+ \cdot A^-$" configurations, the excited (charge transfer) state being the more highly polarized. The excited state can be symbolized as $(D^+ \cdot A^-)^*$ and the ground state as $D \cdot A$. The stabilizing energy in the ground state, associated with resonance, can be called the charge transfer binding energy.

   In conclusion let us review the desired properties of a trapping state in a photosynthetic unit. Whatever its nature, it should be (or should lead efficiently to) a state that is intrinsically long-lived and photochemically reactive as an electron donor or acceptor. These requirements may be met by $n\pi^*$, triplet, and charge transfer states. The functions of trapping energy and initiating photochemistry could of course be divided between two different states, for example as follows:

singlet state (lifetime about $10^{-9}$ sec)

*(Trapping of energy)*

triplet state ($\sim 10^{-3}$ sec)                                        [9.3.4]

*(Start of photochemistry)*

charge transfer state.


## 9.4  Ionization and Conduction

The properties of inorganic crystals have been described satisfactorily on the basis of the orbitals of the outer electrons overlapping completely and extending throughout the crystal.  As a result of this confluence the energy levels corresponding to these orbitals are spread into bands, the ground state giving a "valence band" and the excited states giving "conduction bands."  For a crystal containing $N$ units (atoms or molecules) the bands represent $N$-fold splitting of the energy levels.  In the unexcited crystal the outer electrons are confined to the valence band.  In a conductor the valence band is not completely filled (the filling is dictated by the Pauli principle), and electrons in this band are free to move through the crystal.  In an insulator the valence band is entirely filled and the migration of charge is blocked.  In a semiconductor a few electrons are excited to a conduction band and a few positive holes (electron vacancies) are thereby generated in the valence band.  Both the electrons and the holes may then be able to move in the crystal, and a small conductivity can be observed.

The migration of electrons and holes in a semiconductor can be illustrated by a crude analogy in which the valence and conduction bands are represented by two billiard tables, one suspended above the other.  The lower table is entirely filled with billiard balls, so that none of them can move.  The upper table is empty.  Now if one ball is elevated to the upper table, that ball can move, and the vacancy on the lower table can also move.  If the upper table is changed from a billiard to a pool table (that is, endowed with pockets) another possibility is illustrated; namely, the trapping that can occur at a site of affinity for the carrier.

In semiconducting crystals the electrons may become trapped, leaving the holes free to move (*p*-type), or vice versa (*n*-type).  The traps are characteristically flaws in the crystal that have electrostatic affinity for negative or positive charge.  They arise from structural irregularities and from the presence of foreign atoms or molecules.  Once trapped, an electron or hole can become free again by absorbing a quantum of vibrational or radiative energy from its surroundings. The population of charge carriers is determined by four processes: excitation of electrons into the conduction band, de-excitation (recombination of electrons and holes, with the electrons returning to the valence band), and trapping and untrapping.

The excitation in "dark" semiconduction is caused by thermal agitation. The electrical resistance is accordingly an exponential function of temperature and of the energy gap $\Delta E$ between the valence and conduction bands:

$$\log R = A + B\left(\frac{\Delta E}{T}\right). \qquad [9.4.1]$$

The energy gap can thus be determined experimentally by measuring $R$ as a function of $T$. The appropriate value of the constant $B$ depends on the nature of electron or hole trapping.

Organic molecular crystals behave like semiconductors, showing thermal conductivity according to Equation [9.4.1] and also showing photoconductivity. In the latter process electrons are excited to a conducting state through absorption of light quanta, and the de-excitation is sometimes accompanied by delayed fluorescence. A related phenomenon is the light emission that can be induced in a preparation, after illumination, by heating it. The heating presumably liberates trapped electrons and allows recombination of electrons and holes. Analysis of this thermoluminescence, to determine the rate of untrapping as a function of temperature, yields the energy difference between a trapped and a conducting electron (that is, the trap depth).

Considerable effort has gone into the description of organic semiconductors along the lines suggested by the pre-existing theory of inorganic semiconductors such as germanium. In this extension a valence band was imagined to arise from an overlapping of the molecular $\pi$ orbitals, and a conduction band from overlapping $\pi^*$ orbitals. Eventually it was made clear by C. G. B. Garrett, Kasha, and others that this picture is inappropriate for organic molecular crystals. There is no evidence that the lower (molecular) excited states in a molecular crystal can fuse to form conduction bands. These molecular levels are involved in the visible and near ultraviolet optical transitions, and their fusion in a crystal should lead to a radical change in the absorption spectrum. In actuality the absorption spectra of organic molecules such as anthracene are not grossly different in the crystal and vapor states. The low mobilities of charge carriers in some organic crystals also weigh against the involvement of conduction bands.

Energy sufficient to ionize a single molecule can of course produce conductivity, and it is possible that the higher excited states, analogous to excited states in atoms, can form conduction bands in a molecular crystal. The orbitals of the lower excited states, about 1–3 ev above the ground state, are more closely confined to the individual molecules and do not overlap greatly with those of neighboring molecules. Thus, the lower states cannot form well-developed conduction bands. They can form exciton bands as a result of dipole interactions, but such bands afford migration of excitation quanta and not of electrons or holes.

The fact remains that organic crystals exhibit a feeble semiconductivity and photoconductivity that must be explained by some mechanism. Typical values of conductivity in organic crystals are about $10^{-4}$–$10^{-18}$ ohm$^{-1}$ cm$^{-1}$ at room temperature, in contrast to about $10^5$ ohm$^{-1}$ cm$^{-1}$ for metals and $10^{-2}$ ohm$^{-1}$ cm$^{-1}$ for an inorganic semiconductor such as germanium. The low conductivity in molecular crystals is due partly to a reduced mobility of the charge carriers but mainly to a vastly reduced number of carriers. The reduction in mobility introduces a factor of about $10^{-3}$–$10^{-7}$.

A general model for organic semiconduction and photoconduction must incorporate electronic excitation of a molecule (perhaps followed by promotion to a higher excited state through a two-quantum process), transfer of an electron to a neighboring molecule (dissociation), and further separation of the electron and hole in response to a weak external field (conduction). The essential problem is to understand the nature of the conducting state and the mechanism by which it is entered.

Of the three processes, excitation, dissociation, and conduction, our understanding of the third is limited mainly to speculation within the framework of physical theory. A seemingly reasonable view is as follows. If the conduction is not by way of a well-defined conduction band, the mobile electrons (or holes) may be thought of as excess particles in a molecular matrix. These particles may be obliged to penetrate energy barriers that represent the confinement of electron orbitals to single molecules. The movement of the carriers is then a migratory process (as described by R. C. Nelson, D. D. Eley, and others) that involves repeated penetration of energy barriers. The penetration is by tunneling (as allowed in quantum theory) rather than by surmounting each barrier. In the absence of a polarizing external field the electrons and holes may become widely separated through a random migration of this kind. When an electric field is applied the drift becomes oriented in the direction of the field and a flow of current is observed.

An initial excitation of electrons is required in order for conduction to occur. The first step in photoconduction is of course the promotion of a molecule to an excited state corresponding to the act of light absorption. The initial act in semiconduction is less certain. The energy gap, $\Delta E$ in Equation [9.4.1], can hopefully be correlated with a known molecular excitation. For many substances, including phthalocyanin and porphyrins, $\Delta E$ is about the same as the energy of the lowest singlet excited state. For other substances a correlation with the lowest triplet state is observed. In particular, $\Delta E$ for crystalline Chl is 1.44 ev, corresponding to 860 m$\mu$ (compare Table 8.1). Values reported by different investigators often differ by as much as a factor of two; it is clear that more careful work is needed if the first excited state in semiconduction is to be identified either as a known singlet or triplet state.

At this writing it appears that much of the work purporting to deal with conduction *in* molecular crystals such as anthracene has actually dealt with conduction *on* the crystals. Surface conduction, abetted by the presence of electrodes and other impurities, has provided the major part of the photocurrent in many experiments, especially where the actinic light has been absorbed principally in the outermost layer of the material. The characteristics of this surface conduction are amenable to a model in which a conducting state is entered directly from the lowest excited singlet or triplet state.

A few recent experiments with anthracene, designed to discriminate between bulk and surface conduction, have led to a different picture for the processes by which charge carriers are generated. First R. G. Kepler, through a technique of pulsed photoconductivity measurement, established that the charge carrier mobility *in* anthracene is 0.3 to 2 cm$^2$/volt sec, depending on the direction of the current relative to the crystal axes. Electrons and holes have roughly the same mobility. This information was a prerequisite to the computation of charge carrier concentrations from values of the photocurrent. It could then be shown that the kinetics of photoconduction in highly purified anthracene are understandable if the generation of charge carriers is presumed to involve a biphotonic event: the interaction of two excitons to produce a higher excited state. The kinetics of delayed fluorescence in anthracene, and the excitation of blue fluorescence by red actinic light (see Section 9.2), also implicate biphotonic processes. D. R. Kearns has measured photoconduction in purified anthracene, using a wavelength of ultraviolet actinic light that is absorbed only weakly and hence penetrates the entire sample. Excitation throughout the bulk of the crystal, and not preferentially at the surface, was thereby assured. Upon comparing theoretical and experimental values for the efficiency of charge carrier production, Kearns concluded that the formation of a conducting state requires the summed energy of two singlet excitations (6.4 ev). A singlet-triplet interaction (combined energy 4.9 ev) is marginally able, or perhaps unable to afford conduction, and a triplet-triplet interaction (3.6 ev) is insufficient. These conclusions are consistent with an ionization potential of about 5 ev for anthracene.

The foregoing inferences about conduction in anthracene may turn out to be inapplicable to conduction in ionic dyes. Nelson has investigated conduction as a function of temperature in some cationic dyes for which the electronic energy levels are well-established. A simple application of conduction band theory does not yield reasonable values for both the energy gap and the charge carrier mobility. Sensible conclusions can be drawn, however, if the trapping of electrons or holes is incorporated as an essential part of the mechanism. A cycle of excitation and de-excitation is envisioned that involves ionization, trapping of electrons or holes, and recombination of the oppositely charged trapped and free species. Based on this model, the computed mobilities are reasonable for electrons or holes in molecular crystals, while the energy gap can be identified with an electronic transition into the lowest excited singlet state.

A necessary step leading to conduction is the conversion of an excited state to a dissociated state in which an electron has moved from one molecule to another. The problem in understanding this event is one of energies and probabilities. Direct ionization, into an "atomic" conduction band or into the ionization continuum, could well be the mechanism in anthracene where the summed energies of two singlet excitons appear to be needed for conduction. In dyes such as those studied by Nelson, characterized by considerable electron orbital overlap, dissociation might occur from the first excited singlet state by the tunneling mechanism described earlier. The efficiency of dissociation by this avenue, beginning with a molecule in its lowest excited singlet state, depends on the relative probabilities of two events: return of the excited electron to the ground state and transfer of this electron, by tunneling, to a neighboring molecule. In aggregates of dyes having a strong $\pi\pi^*$ transition, the lifetime of singlet excitation is about $10^{-9}$ sec. For an intermolecular energy barrier about 3 ev high and 4 Å thick the penetration time can be considerably shorter, on the order of $10^{-12}$ sec or less. Efficient dissociation by this mechanism thus appears to be feasible. The tunneling model becomes even more atrractive for migration of electrons after the initial dissociation. The excited electron is then stable toward de-excitation because it is associated with a molecule whose original ground state is occupied.

Another factor that can assist dissociation is the existence of traps (sites of affinity for electrons or holes) that can lower the ionization energy by several electron volts. This sort of facilitation may occur in the photo-ionization of tri-$p$-tolylamine. The ionization potential of gaseous tri-$p$-tolylamine is 8–12 ev. In a rigid organic solution at 90°K this substance is photo-ionized by 3–5 ev quanta. It has been proposed that electrons are captured by the solvent, leaving the solute in an oxidized state. If this interpretation is correct the electron affinity (or trapping energy) of the solvent amounts to about 6 ev. It can thus be expected that traps will commonly bring ionization within the range of visible light quanta. However, in a similar system involving ionization of tetra-methylphenylenediamine a two-quantum mechanism has been implicated and solvent affinity need not be invoked.

Traps can be provided by impurities or flaws in a crystal; they are probably responsible for the facilitation of surface conduction on "dirty" anthracene. Traps may also exist in more orderly fashion in the form of substances that form charge transfer complexes with the crystal mole-cules. An example of the latter case is an interesting system that has been studied by D. R. Kearns, G. Tollin, and M. Calvin. The system consists of phthalocyanin (PC) as a semiconductor and quinones, especially $o$-chloranil (CH), as agents having electron affinity. Dry films of PC, with or without a coating of CH, were examined in the dark and under light absorbed by PC. It was observed that the semi- and photoconduc-tivity of PC increased by factors of $10^7$ and $10^5$, respectively, when CH was applied. Electrostatic measurements showed that electrons were trans-ferred from PC to CH in the dark, and this transfer was increased revers-ibly by illumination. Electron spin resonance measurements showed a large signal in the dark that was *decreased* reversibly by light. These results were interpreted as follows:

$$\text{Dark: PC} + \text{CH} \rightleftarrows \text{PC}^+ + \text{CH}^-.$$
$$\text{Light: PC}^* + \text{CH}^- \rightleftarrows \text{PC}^+ + \text{CH}^=. \qquad [9.4.2]$$

The charge carrier is $PC^+$, or more accurately, the hole that is associated with PC and symbolized as $PC^+$. The source of the ESR signal is $CH^-$, and the photo-ionization is facilitated mainly by the presence of $CH^-$ as an electron acceptor. The quantum efficiency for carrier production is about 100% in (PC + CH) and less than 10% in PC alone. The increased conductivity endowed by CH was ascribed mainly to the enhanced life-time of the carriers, recombination of electrons and holes being prevented by the trapping action of CH and $CH^-$.

Another system of this sort, a sandwich made of Chl and carotene, has been studied by W. Arnold and H. K. Maclay. In this system electrons move from carotene to Chl in the light. Both components are photo-conductors, but there was no evidence for an enormous change in con-ductivity when the two components were placed in contact with each other. The kinetics of light-induced polarization of the sandwich, and of photoconductivity, showed the participation of electron traps.

There is still considerable argument concerning whether the conduc-tivity of hydrated proteins is ionic or electronic in nature. B. Rosenberg and others seem to have shown convincingly that water is not lost by hydrolysis (as it should be if ionic conduction prevails) when a current is passed through hydrated hemoglobin.  But other reports indicate that photoconductivity is lost at liquid helium temperature; this may or may not rule out electronic conduction, depending on the mechanism of ionization.

Arnold and others have amassed considerable evidence that photosynthetic tissues behave like organic semiconductors.  The possible importance of this behavior for photosynthesis will be examined in Chapter 12.  From its optical manifestations the conduction in photosynthetic systems, sensitized by Chl, appears to be electronic.

# Physical Aspects of Photosynthesis

# 10. Introduction

THE PHYSICAL problems of photosynthesis were delineated in Part I, and some of the language and meaning of molecular physics was developed in Part II.   We are thus in a position to evaluate what is known about the primary physical events in photosynthesis.

Our knowledge in this area rests largely on the application of optical techniques.   The most fruitful procedures at present are the measurement of emitted light, the study of minute changes in absorption spectra, and the determination of excitation spectra for various processes.   The technical and interpretive problems arising in such measurements will be the subject of Chapter 11.

In Chapter 12 we shall begin with evidence bearing on the state of aggregation of Chl and BChl *in vivo;* this will afford an estimation of the kinds and strengths of molecular interactions that prevail in the photosynthetic unit.   Manifestations of photo-ionization, electron trapping, and conduction will then be described, and the significance of these "solid state" phenomena will be evaluated.   Finally, the evidence for migration of excitation energy will be reviewed and the potentialities of energy transfer analyzed.

Chapter 13 will deal first with a variety of problems connected with fluorescence of Chl and BChl *in vivo*.   The relation between yield and lifetime of fluorescence and the dependence of fluorescence intensity on several parameters (time, exciting wavelength and intensity, and physiological factors) has had important consequences for the development of ideas about the mechanism of photosynthesis.   The role of the triplet state of Chl will be assessed in connection with photosynthesis and with photochemical processes that are deleterious to plants.   It will then be appropriate to review the development of Franck's theories; these are especially interesting because they represent genuine efforts to coordinate physical theory with the biochemical phenomenology of the subject.

# 11. Optical Techniques in The Study of Photosynthesis

## 11.1 Measurement

THREE TECHNIQUES will be described in this section: the measurement of emitted light, the recording of minute absorption transients, and the determination of excitation spectra for light-induced phenomena.

In measuring emitted light it is of interest to determine the intensity as functions of wavelength and time. The experimental problem is to detect weak emission while shielding the detector from the much brighter exciting light. The instrumental arrangement is shown in generalized form in Figure 11.1. Blockage of the detector from the exciting light is facilitated if lamp, sample, and detector do not lie on a single optic axis.

An attempt to measure everything (excitation spectrum, emission spectrum, and emission lifetime) with a single instrument leads to compromises that reduce the quality of the measurement. It is usually more practicable to measure the spectrum without regard to lifetime, the time distribution of the total emission, et cetera. The details of the arrangement then depend on what is to be measured.

Four useful arrangements are shown in Figure 11.2. The first (a) is designed to measure the time course of short-lived emission. The detector is designed to respond rapidly (response time $\sim 10^{-9}$ sec); this can be achieved with a photomultiplier, a low-impedance amplifier, and an oscilloscope to record the output of the amplifier. The response time can be no less than $RC$, where $R$ is the resistance through which the photocurrent passes and $C$ is the inevitable "stray" input capacitance of the amplifier. If $R$ is made small to obtain a fast response, the voltage generated by the photocurrent is correspondingly small and more amplification is needed. A sufficiently brief flash can be obtained by passing the light of a xenon flash lamp through a pulsed Kerr Cell. A Kerr Cell transmits or blocks polarized light in response to a voltage that polarizes the material of which it is made; a pulse of polarizing voltage can be synchronized with the flash emitted by the lamp. By this method one can

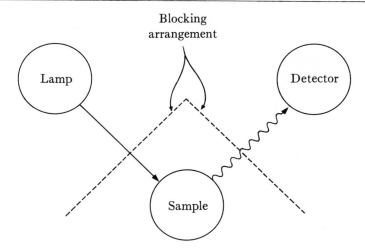

Blocking
arrangement

Lamp

Detector

Sample

FIGURE 11.1.  *General arrangement for the excitation and detection of emitted light.*

study emission lifetimes of about $10^{-9}$ sec.  The intensity of emission
decays rapidly with time (exponentially for fluorescence in competition
with first-order quenching of the singlet state) and so it is difficult to
follow the time course of emission beyond about $10^{-8}$ sec.

The time course of long-lived emission can be followed with a mechanical phosphoroscope (Figure 11.2c) which allows measurement at a con-
trollable time after excitation.   An alternative to the rotating discs is a
system that pumps a liquid sample past the lamp and then past the
detector.   With a sliding shutter (Figure 11.2d) one can measure all of
the light emitted after a certain time (the time needed for operation of the
shutter).

The least time that can be resolved by rotating phosphoroscopes and
shutters is about $10^{-5}$ sec.   There is thus an interval in the emission lifetime, between about $10^{-5}$ and $10^{-8}$ sec, that is especially difficult to
measure.

The arrangement shown in Figure 11.2b allows measurement of the
steady emission under continuous excitation as well as the time course
when the lamp is turned on and off.   This is the usual method of determining the spectrum of the emission without regard to its lifetime.   Fluorescence and phosphorescence measured in this way must be distinguished
on the basis of wavelength.   In photosynthetic tissues the total short-
lived emission ($\sim 10^{-8}$ sec lifetime) is far brighter than the total longer-
lived component.

The filter $F_2$ in Figure 11.2b reduces the amount of stray exciting light
that reaches the detector.   In general the best choice of monochromators

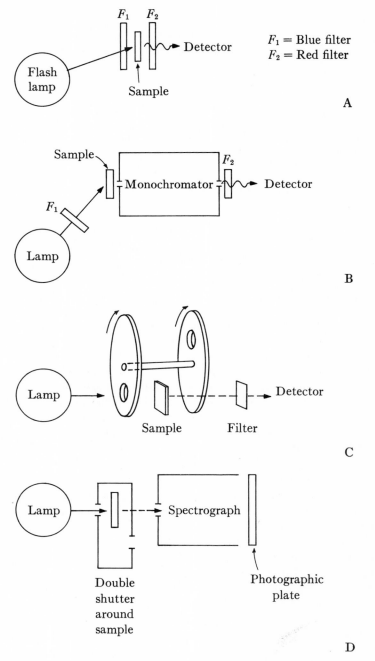

$F_1$ = Blue filter
$F_2$ = Red filter

A

B

C

D

FIGURE 11.2. *Four useful arrangements for the study of fluorescence and phosphorescence. Further description in text.*

and filters (including interference filters) is dictated by the ratio of emitted to exciting light, by the parameter of greatest interest (wavelength or time), and by the geometry of the apparatus. In Figure 11.2c, for example, the weakness of the phosphorescence to be measured necessitates the measurement of light from a large area of the sample. It is difficult to meet this requirement if a monochromator is in the system.

An excellent "continuous" lamp for the excitation of fluorescence in photosynthetic tissues is the tungsten-iodine lamp that has become popular in photography under the name "sun gun." Greater intensity can be attained, especially in the ultraviolet, with a high pressure xenon or xenon-mercury arc, but unless special precautions are taken these arc lamps are not stable enough for precise measurement of the time course of emission.

The fluorescence of Chl can be detected with any of a variety of photomultipliers. To measure the longer wave phosphorescence, and also the emission from BChl, it is necessary to use an infrared-sensitive photomultiplier such as the RCA 7102, a suitable photographic plate, or a photoconductive cell. Lead sulfide cells are used in many commercial spectrophotometers for measurement in the near infrared. The photomultiplier has the disadvantage that it is insensitive beyond about 1100 m$\mu$. Also the high dark current of an infrared-sensitive photomultiplier must be reduced by cooling the instrument, for example, with dry ice.

A different way of measuring the average (or most probable) lifetime of emission is the technique of phase fluorimetry. This method resembles that of Figure 11.2a except that the intensity of the exciting light is modulated at a high frequency instead of being a brief flash. The phase of the emitted light lags behind that of the absorbed light by an amount determined by the lifetime of the excited state of the emitter. Thus if the frequency of the intensity modulation is $10^7$ sec$^{-1}$ and the mean lifetime is $10^{-9}$ sec the phase difference will be 1%. The response time of the detecting and amplifying system need not be quite as short as in the method of Figure 11.2a; a time comparable to the frequency of modulation is sufficient. The price paid for this less severe requirement is that the phase method gives only the mean lifetime and no detailed information about the time course of the emission. Phase fluorimetry is illustrated schematically in Figure 11.3. The optical paths from the sample to the detectors $D_T$ and $D_F$ (for the transmitted exciting light and the fluorescent light) must be equal; otherwise this is partly a method of measuring the speed of light. The intensity modulation is achieved by applying a high frequency alternating voltage to a Kerr Cell or a quartz crystal. The quartz crystal behaves like a diffraction grating when an electric field is applied; the diffracted light varies in intensity with the applied voltage.

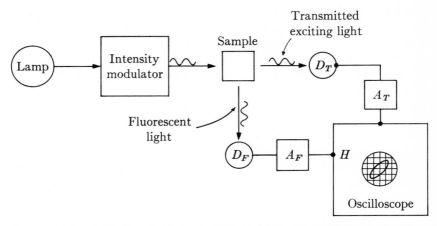

FIGURE 11.3. *Apparatus for the measurement of fluorescence lifetime by the phase method. $D_T$ and $A_T$ are the detector and the amplifier for the transmitted light; $D_F$ and $A_F$ are those for the fluorescent light. The outputs of $A_F$ and $A_T$ can be put on the horizontal and vertical plates of a cathode ray oscilloscope. If these signals are in phase the display will be a straight line. An elliptic pattern shows the phase difference between the two signals.*

Minute absorbancy changes are measured by techniques that were mentioned briefly in Section 2.1 (see Figure 2.1). The reversible changes that are of interest for photosynthesis are quite small: the transmittance usually varies by 1% or less, corresponding to a change in optical density of about 0.005 or less. As in the measurement of fluorescence, an arrangement must be used such that the detector (which now measures monochromatic light transmitted by the sample) is insensitive to the exciting light. This is achieved by using complementary filters, by alternating the excitation and the measurement, or by measuring modulated light with an A. C. amplifier that is insensitive to the steady exciting light.

The appropriate experimental design is governed by the sizes of the effects to be measured, by the time resolution that is desired, by the degree to which the measuring light might cause excitation and thus pre-empt the function of the exciting light, and by such considerations as the turbidity and stability of the sample.

A relatively simple arrangement is shown in Figure 11.4. A single measuring beam passes through the sample and generates a signal in the photomultiplier. The steady component of this light signal is balanced electrically, and the small variations are amplified and recorded.† The

† The steady signal can also be compensated with a second light signal, drawn from the same measuring lamp and generated by a second detector. This method neutralizes fluctuations in the measuring lamp but is more cumbersome. With a D. C.-operated tungsten lamp such neutralization is unnecessary.

detector is shielded from the exciting light by means of complementary color filters. No devices are introduced to compensate for fluctuations in the measuring lamp or for nonessential changes in the sample. With reasonable precautions such as a well regulated D. C. power supply for the measuring lamp this method can be used to detect changes of the order of 0.001 optical density units in nonturbid samples. If repeated responses are evaluated by a Computer of Average Transients the signal: noise ratio is readily improved tenfold or more and minute changes can be detected in turbid samples.

Aside from its simplicity, the arrangement of Figure 11.4 has the virtue that measurements can be made continuously before, during, and after excitation. The only restrictions on the time-resolution are those imposed by the exciting lamp and the measuring system. By using a flash lamp for excitation and an oscilloscope for recording, one can readily observe the kinetics of absorption transients that rise or decay in $10^{-5}$ sec. The observation of faster events is limited mainly by the intensity of the flash lamp; this limits the amount of a photochemical change that can be produced in a short time. If a response time shorter than about 0.3 sec is not needed, several commercial spectrophotometers can be adapted satisfactorily to the method of Fig. 11.4 by introducing a path for the exciting beam.

The more elaborate arrangement of Figure 11.5 has been used extensively by Duysens and by Kok. Here the measuring light is split into two beams, one passing through the sample. The beams are made to fall alternately, with equal intensity, on the detector. This alternation can be caused by a rotating sector that also provides for alternation between

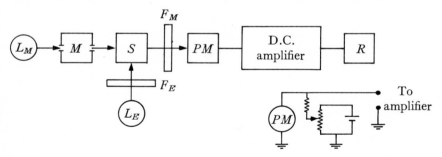

Single beam

FIGURE 11.4. *A single-beam instrument for amplifying and recording light induced absorbancy changes. $L_M$ and $L_E$ are sources of the measuring and exciting light. M is a monochromator. S is the sample to be studied. $F_M$ and $F_E$ are complementary color filters. PM is a photomultiplier. A D. C. amplifier and a recorder R complete the system. The steady component of the photosignal is nullified by the electrical circuit shown.*

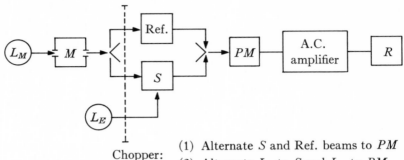

Chopper:
(1) Alternate $S$ and Ref. beams to $PM$
(2) Alternate $L_E$ to $S$ and $L_M$ to $PM$

Split beam

FIGURE 11.5. *A split-beam difference spectrophotometer for measuring absorption transients. A chopper, shown as a dashed line, passes the measuring beam alternately through the sample and through a reference path. Excitation is alternated with measurement by the same chopper. When the two beams reaching the photomultiplier are of unequal intensity an A. C. signal is generated.*

excitation and measurement. Any imbalance generated by a transient change in the sample appears as a modulated signal that is fed into an A. C. amplifier. Temporal alternation between excitation and measurement is of course not the only way in which the measuring system can be made unresponsive to the exciting light. Complementary filters or steady excitation coupled with A. C. measurement can also be used. The technique of Figure 11.5 permits A. C. amplification tuned to the frequency at which the beams are alternated. A considerable amount of noise (such as that due to fluctuations in the exciting lamp) can thus be suppressed. The time-discrimination is of course limited; transients can only be followed if they occur slowly in comparison with the period of alternation of the beams.

A higher degree of compensation is afforded by the double beam method of Figure 11.6, used extensively in Chance's laboratory. Here a pair of monochromatic beams of different wavelengths, originating from a single lamp, are passed alternately through the sample and on to the detector. The change in absorbancy due to excitation is generally different at the two wavelengths; ideally one wavelength is neutral (no absorbancy change). The exciting light thus causes a modulated imbalance in the light signal; this is amplified and recorded. The steady exciting light is ignored by the A. C. amplifier. This method compensates for gradual changes in the scattering properties of the sample, provided that the two measuring wavelengths are not too widely separated. It is especially useful with turbid samples such as cell suspensions. As in the method of Figure 11.5, the time resolution is limited by the frequency of alternation of the two beams. Alternation faster than about 0.01 sec is hard to achieve mechanically without introducing spurious photoelectrical signals.

For continuous exciting light a good compromise between brightness and stability is offered by the tungsten-iodine lamp in the visible (and near infrared) and by the deuterium arc lamp in the ultraviolet. Special stabilizing circuits, that permit the use of high pressure xenon arcs, have been designed recently.

With any of the foregoing arrangements the intrinsic signal/noise ratio of the detector sets a limit on the sensitivity of the instrument. The high frequency components of noise can be removed if the measuring system is deliberately given a slow response, either by inserting a suitable condenser in the amplifying circuit or by using a sluggish recorder. Also the signal/noise ratio inherent in a photomultiplier improves (for a given photocurrent) as the square root of the intensity of the measuring light. But if the measuring light is made too bright it will cause significant excitation of the sample and thus reduce the effect of the exciting light. The degree to which the measuring light excites the sample can be determined easily by the method shown in Figure 11.7. A neutral filter (providing, say, an eight-fold attenuation) is placed in the measuring beam, either before or after the sample (at positions $A$ and $B$ respectively). The only difference produced by moving the filter is a change in the illumination of the sample by the measuring beam. If the response to the exciting light is independent of the position of the filter, it can be concluded that the measuring beam has no stimulating effect. Considerable stimulation by the measuring beam has been unavoidable in the detection of rapid reversible light-

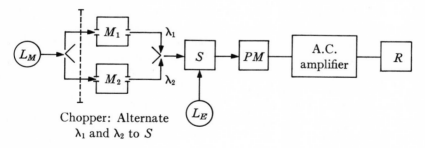

Chopper: Alternate
$\lambda_1$ and $\lambda_2$ to $S$

Double beam

FIGURE 11.6. *A double beam difference spectrophotometer. Two measuring beams of different wavelengths pass alternately through the sample and on to the detector. After the beams have been balanced, an unequal change in absorbancy at the two wavelengths produces an A. C. signal.*

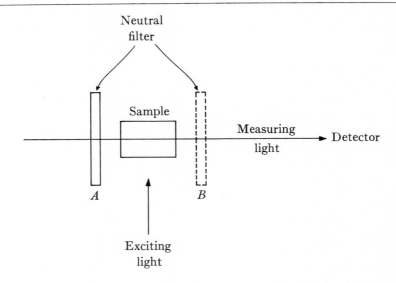

FIGURE 11.7. *A technique for deciding whether the measuring light produces significant excitation in comparison with the effect of the exciting light. The light-induced change is measured with a neutral filter at position A and then at position B.*

induced changes in chloroplasts and algae.    This limitation can be relieved greatly by the computer technique for improving the signal to noise ratio.

The determination of excitation spectra for light emission and for photo-chemical events entails all of the techniques thus far described, with the added complication that the exciting light must be monochromatic.    The wavelength of the exciting light must be variable and the intensity must be known, at least in arbitrary units proportional to energy, as a function of wavelength.    Monochromatic exciting light can be produced with a monochromator or with a set of interference filters.    Its intensity is best calibrated by means of a thermopile in conjunction with a sensitive galvanometer.    The calibration can be translated from energy flux to quantum flux by multiplying each energy value (galvanometer deflection) by the corresponding wavelength.    A reliable calibration is obtained most easily if the spectral emission of the exciting lamp is "smooth"; an arc lamp having strong spectral emission lines superimposed on a continuous background should be avoided if possible.

## 11.2   Interpretation

In this section we shall consider some common sources of misinterpreta-tion encountered in the foregoing measurements.

Three sources of error arise often in the measurement of emitted light; these are listed below together with the usual ways of dealing with them.

1. Reabsorption of the emitted light by the sample.   Use dilute preparations or make appropriate corrections.

2. Fluorescence of sample holders, filters, et cetera.   Use quartz where possible.   Measure with an inert preparation as a control.

3. Stimulation of the detector by the exciting light.   As a control use an inert preparation having about the same light scattering properties as the sample.

The common sources of error and their recognition in measuring small absorbancy changes are as follows.

1. Stimulation of the sample by the measuring beam.   Apply the test shown in Figure 11.7.

2. Superposition of two or more reactions at one wavelength.   Discriminate the reactions kinetically, or by their dependence on exciting light intensity, or through the use of chemical or physiological inhibitors. A thermal artifact (change of transmission resulting. from a change in temperature) can usually be distinguished by its failure to exhibit light saturation, by its exponential rise and decay characteristics, and by its insensitivity to chemical inhibition.

3. Fluorescence mistaken for a decrease in absorbancy.   Between the sample and the detector place an interference filter that transmits the wavelength of the measuring beam, and see if the apparent absorbancy change is reduced strongly.

4. A change in light-scattering properties of the sample mistaken for a change in absorbancy.   Alter the geometry so as to collect more or less of the scattered light and see if the change is affected.

5. Stimulation of the detector by the exciting light.   Measure with an inert preparation having the same scattering properties as the sample. This effect is easily distinguished by its kinetics and by its independence of the measuring wavelength.

A great deal has been written about the pitfalls encountered in the determination of excitation spectra but the literature continues to abound with reports of worthless or misleading data.

In general it is not appropriate to determine the size of a response as a function of wavelength using fixed intensity (energy or quantum flux) of the exciting light.   This can only be useful if the size of the response is an accurately known function (for example, a linear function) of exciting light intensity.   A safer procedure is to choose a standard submaximal response and to determine the intensity needed to elicit this response at each wavelength.   The resulting action spectrum should be expressed in units of quantum flux.   If it is to be compared with an absorption spec-

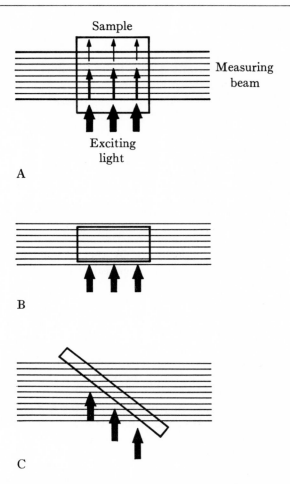

FIGURE 11.8.  *Three geometries of measuring beam, exciting beam, and sample in difference spectrophotometry.  The distortion of an excitation spectrum due to attenuation of the exciting light is greatest in case (a) and least in case (c).*

trum of the same preparation, the latter should be plotted not as optical density but as per cent absorbed *vs.* wavelength.

The screening effect of inert pigments will superimpose (in an inverted form) the spectrum of these pigments upon the spectrum of the active pigments; this effect should be recognized when it occurs.

A commonly overlooked cause of distortion of excitation spectra has to do with the penetration of the sample by the exciting light.  If fluorescence is being measured, this penetration factor influences the degree to which the emitted light is reabsorbed.  If a saturable phenomenon (such as an ESR signal) is being recorded, the response will be truncated when most of the exciting light is being absorbed by a small fraction of the preparation. This occurs when the illumination is above saturation in the small fraction and below saturation elsewhere.

The penetration error can be especially severe when an absorbancy change is being measured. Figure 11.8 shows how this can come about with a poorly chosen geometry, and how it can be alleviated. In example (a) the exciting light is absorbed in large measure by material that is not in the path of the measuring beam; for observational purposes this material is inert. The situation is improved in example (b), and still more so in (c). Geometry (c) can lead, however, to errors arising from uncertainty concerning the refraction of light within the sample holder.

The effect of the penetration error is to generate minima in an excitation spectrum where the maxima ought to be (that is, at the peaks of absorption) and vice versa. In addition to choosing a "good" optical geometry, one should observe the shape of an excitation spectrum under progressive dilution of the sample. When the light-absorbing pigments are dilute enough the penetration error disappears, and the shape of the spectrum becomes a correct reflection of the activity of the exciting light.

In conclusion, a single technique will be described for the determination of the quantum efficiency of a photochemical event. The event is signaled by a change in absorbancy at a certain wavelength, and the change in molar extinction coefficient ($\Delta\epsilon$) is known at this wavelength for the transformation (such as oxidation of a cytochrome) involved in the reaction.

The experimental arrangement is shown in Figure 11.9, and the information obtained is indicated in Figure 11.10. The exciting light is monochromatic and its intensity at the sample is known in einstein/cm² sec.†

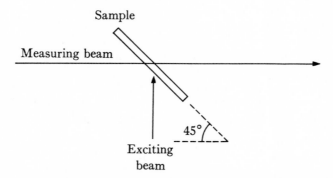

FIGURE 11.9. *A convenient geometry for determining the quantum efficiency of a light-induced process signalled by an absorbancy change.*

† One einstein/sec equals $1.2 \times 10^8/\lambda$ watts, where $\lambda$ is the wavelength in m$\mu$.

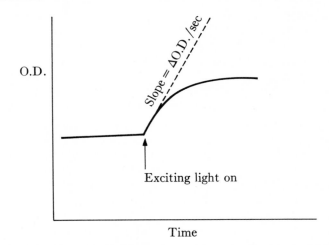

FIGURE 11.10.   *Trace of optical density vs. time in measurement of quantum efficiency.   The efficiency can be calculated from the initial slope of the absorbancy change.*

Calibration of the exciting light is done with a thermopile-galvanometer arrangement that has been calibrated with a standard lamp.   The exciting wavelength is chosen to coincide with an absorption peak of the presumedly active pigment (for example, the long wave band of Chl).

The fraction of the incident exciting light that is absorbed by the active pigment is estimated from an absorption spectrum of the sample as viewed along the axis of the exciting beam (see Figure 11.11).   The computation is simple if absorption by the pigment accounts for most of the attenuation of the exciting beam.   If scattering, reflection, and absorption by inert pigments cause a significant part of the attenuation one must resort to a more sophisticated calculation than the one indicated in the Figure.

Now if the incident intensity is $J$ einstein/cm² sec and the fraction absorbed is $f$, light is being absorbed at a rate $Jf$ einstein/sec for each cm² of the preparation.†   Meanwhile the photochemical reaction gives initially a certain $\Delta$O. D. per second.   With a molar differential extinction coefficient $\Delta\epsilon$, the photochemical conversion amounts to

$$\Delta C = \frac{\Delta \text{O. D.}}{S \, \Delta\epsilon},$$   [11.2.1]

where $\Delta C$ is the change in molar concentration of the substance converted, $S$ is the thickness of the sample along the axis of the measuring beam, and the units of $\Delta\epsilon$ are $M^{-1}\,cm^{-1}$.   The number of moles converted per cm² of

† The area in cm² is the projected area perpendicular to the axis of the exciting beam.

projected area perpendicular to the axis of the measuring beam is

$$\Delta n = S \cdot (\Delta \text{ moles/cm}^3) = S\, \Delta C \times 10^{-3}. \qquad [11.2.2]$$

The number of moles converted per cm² per second is therefore

$$\Delta n/\text{sec} = S \left( \frac{\Delta \text{O. D.}/\text{sec}}{S\, \Delta \epsilon} \right) \times 10^{-3} \text{ or } \left( \frac{\Delta \text{O. D.}/\text{sec}}{\Delta \epsilon} \right) \times 10^{-3}. \quad [11.2.3]$$

This value is to be compared with the rate of light absorption, $Jf$ einstein/ cm² sec. Area is used in two ways in these computations: perpendicular to the measuring beam on one hand and to the exciting beam on the other. For the geometry shown in Figure 11.9 the density of the sample is the same as seen from either of these perspectives.† The area factor can therefore be cancelled without error, and the quantum requirement is

$$q = \frac{Jf}{\Delta n/\text{sec}} = \frac{1000\, Jf\, \Delta \epsilon}{\Delta \text{O. D.}/\text{sec}}, \qquad [11.2.4]$$

in units of einsteins per mole or quanta per molecule converted. The quantum efficiency is of course the reciprocal of the quantum requirement.

Two precautions should be kept in mind when a quantum requirement is determined in this way. First, the extinction coefficient of a substance *in vivo* may not equal that of the extracted and purified substance. The equating of one to the other is valid only in the light of supporting evidence. Second, the use of the initial slope in the curve of ΔO. D. *vs.* time is predicated on the idea that during the initial part of the photochemical reaction the effects of any secondary reactions (such as a back-

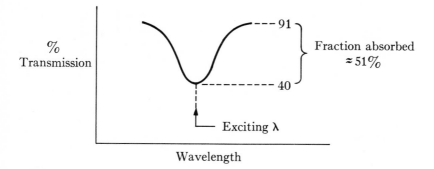

FIGURE 11.11. *Determination of the approximate fraction of the exciting light absorbed by a sample in a measurement of quantum efficiency. Further explanation in text.*

† This condition is also fulfilled when the sample is held in a cuvette of square cross section, each face being perpendicular to one of the light beams.

reaction, or further conversion of the product) are negligible. This may not be true if the preparation has not been allowed to become thoroughly dark-adapted prior to the measurement. An error can also arise if a second photochemical reaction interacts quickly and strongly with the reaction being studied. If, for example, the primary excitation were used competitively for several processes, the significance of the observed quantum efficiency of one process could be unclear.

In any case one should be sure that a definable process is being studied. A quantum efficiency or an excitation spectrum for fluorescence is of uncertain value if the light emitted by two different pigments is collected and measured indiscriminately.

# 12. Excitation Energy and Electric Charge in the Photosynthetic Unit

## 12.1   The State of Chlorophyll *In Vivo*

THE DEGREE of aggregation and orientation of Chl *in vivo* determines the potentialities of the pigment for conducting excitation energy and electric charge in a photosynthetic unit.   An understanding of the condition of Chl in its natural state is therefore of first importance for speculations about these physical mechanisms.   Information of this kind has been gleaned through chemical analysis, electron microscopy, and optical investigations of chloroplasts and chromatophores.

The morphology of photosynthetic tissues in relation to photosynthetic units was outlined in Section 1.4.   In photosynthetic bacteria the smallest photosynthetic organelle is the chromatophore; according to J. A. Bergeron and R. C. Fuller the relatively small chromatophores of *Chromatium* (about 300 Å in diameter) each contain about 600 molecules of BChl or (see Section 1.4) about 15 photosynthetic units.   In chloroplasts the Chl is confined to grainy lamellar structures; each grain or quantasome could contain about 300 Chl molecules or one photosynthetic unit.   Fragmented bacterial and plant preparations yield, upon differential centrifugation, pigmented particles that seem to correspond to the chromatophores and quantasomes as seen (with the electron microscope) in sections of tissues. This identification appears tacitly in the literature, but it is by no means certain that the extracted "chromatophores" and "quantasomes" are not artifacts generated by disrupting the material.   Extracted quantasomes appear to be oblate spheroids about $100 \times 200$ Å.

In chloroplasts the synthesis of Chl parallels the development of lamellar structure and also the capacity for photosynthesis.   The investigations of J. H. C. Smith, D. von Wettstein, J. A. Schiff, and others have shown clearly the interdependence of these events.   The creation of the final organized structure depends on the availability of Chl as an architectural unit.   In young leaves that have been kept in the dark there is little or

149

no Chl and the lamellar structure is undeveloped.  Protochlorophyll is present, each molecule being bound to a proteinaceous particle that has about the same dimensions as the quantasome of a mature leaf.  Upon exposure to light protochlorophyll is converted to Chl $a$, more of these and other pigments are synthesized, and the lamellar structure begins to develop.  These findings may lack general validity; L. Bogorad and W. Menke have observed lamellar structure in forms of algae that lack Chl.

The lipid and protein components of chloroplasts and chromatophores can be assigned locations with some assurance on the basis of electron microscope images of preparations treated in various ways.  Then if the amount of each major constituent as determined chemically is to fit into the visible structure, some plausible inferences can be drawn about the detailed structure.  The prevailing opinion is that Chl is deployed as a two-dimensional aggregate sandwiched between protein and lipid layers.  The porphyrin "head" of the molecule is bound to protein and the phytyl "tail" extends into the lipid layer.  In chromatophores this arrangement is visualized by Bergeron and Fuller as a spherical shell of BChl between an outer shell of protein and an inner one of lipid.  The shell allows an area of about 200 $Å^2$ for each BChl molecule.  This is enough room without overlapping if the planes of the porphyrin heads are not tangential to the surface of the shell; the area of the head is about 250 $Å^2$.  The "sandwich" distribution of Chl visualized in chloroplasts arose from a conception of alternating protein and lipid layers in the lamellae.  Now that the quantasomes have been recognized the picture of a flat protein-Chl-lipid sandwich is not so compellingly plausible.  Certainly these detailed structural pictures have been overextended, for chromatophores as well as for chloroplasts.  In any case one can conceive that Chl and BChl exist $in$ $vivo$ as two- or three-dimensional aggregates, either in contact with water or protected from water by a lipid-protein environment.

The absorption maxima of Chl and BChl $in$ $vivo$ are at greater wavelengths than the corresponding maxima in solution.  Also the single long wave band $in$ $vitro$ appears as two or more bands $in$ $vivo$.  In green plants and algae the forms of Chl $a$ absorbing at about 673 and 683 m$\mu$ have been associated with photochemical systems II and I respectively (see Section 3.2).  The various BChl types (maxima at 800, 850, and 870–900 m$\mu$) in purple bacteria appear to serve a single photochemical function.

The multiplicity of Chl and BChl bands $in$ $vivo$ could be attributed to different electronic transitions in a single molecule or to different components of the total pigment.  The latter interpretation is correct, as will be shown presently.  Chl or BChl has its absorption maximum at one wavelength or another, depending on its environment.  The determining environmental factor could be the nature of the binding of pigment to protein; it could also be the electric dipole interaction between neighboring pigment molecules.

Several investigators, especially E. E. Jacobs, A. S. Holt, H. J. Trurnit, and A. A. Krasnovskii, have studied the absorption spectra and fluorescence of artificial Chl and BChl aggregates with a view to interpreting the properties of these pigments *in vivo*. The aggregates included amorphous and microcrystalline colloidal suspensions, thin crystalline films, adsorbates (on a variety of substrates including protein), and layers prepared on a water surface. A general property of these aggregates is that the absorption maxima are at greater wavelengths than their counterparts in unimolecular solution. The aggregates thus appear to be suitable models for understanding the *in vivo* spectra. The band shifts are due in part to a wavelength-dependent scattering of light, but this effect is small in comparison with the genuine displacement of the absorption bands.

It was soon recognized that most artificial aggregates or adsorbates of Chl are not fluorescent; the quenching of the fluorescence was ascribed to the adventitious presence of energy sinks. The high efficiency of photosynthesis then shows that the aggregated Chl *in vivo* is remarkably free of such parasitic sinks. Later it became evident that if lipids are present in the artificial systems the Chl is fluorescent. The behavior of Chl in artificial aggregates is then more nearly like that of the weakly fluorescent Chl *in vivo*.

By adding water to a solution of Chl in acetone one can prepare colloidal suspensions of the pigment. The very first particles of aggregated Chl formed in this way have an amorphous appearance; their absorption maximum is at 670–675 m$\mu$ (compare 660 m$\mu$ for the dissolved pigment). The maximum shifts to about 735 m$\mu$ as the particles grow larger. Crystals of Chl prepared in various ways absorb maximally at about 735 m$\mu$.

Layers of Chl on water surfaces are of two kinds. Suppose that a little Chl, dissolved in petroleum ether, is dropped on a water surface and allowed to spread indefinitely. If the resulting rarefied monolayer is compressed, the relation between area and pressure is like that between the volume and pressure of a gas. This kind of relation, suggesting a monolayer of randomly oriented Chl molecules, prevails until the area available to each molecule is only about 100 Å$^2$. At this point the molecules could not be lying flat without overlapping. A further compression causes an apparent transition: the area diminishes to about 70 Å$^2$ per molecule with very little increase in pressure. Arguments about the area and the extinction coefficient of the Chl indicate that the layer is then two molecules thick. The two kinds of layer have been called amorphous and crystalline respectively, probably because the first absorbs maximally at 675 m$\mu$ and the second at 735 m$\mu$ in correspondence with the absorption maxima of amorphous and crystalline colloidal aggregates. The Chl molecules in a rarefied monolayer could be oriented randomly, but in the compressed monolayer just before the transition (at 100 Å² per molecule) the molecules might well be in an orderly arrangement.

The colloidal Chl aggregate and the "amorphous" monolayer, with maximum absorption at 675 mμ, appear to be good models for the state of Chl *in vivo*, whereas the crystalline aggregates and layers are not. By using mixtures of Chl *a*, Chl *b*, and carotene, G. Colmano has made preparations that mimic the absorption spectrum of *Chlorella* almost perfectly.

Spectra of aggregated BChl, studied by Krasnovskii and Jacobs and their colleagues, indicate that the crystalline condition may exist in chromatophores. Crystals and solid films of BChl exhibit absorption bands at about 800 and 850–865 mμ, corresponding to the single band at 770 mμ of BChl in solution. The two bands in the aggregate may be counterparts of the 675 and 735 mμ bands of aggregated Chl *a*. Hydration of a dried BChl film causes another band to appear at 870–890 mμ, apparently at the expense of the 850–865 mμ band. These band systems bear a remarkable correspondence to the absorption bands of BChl *in vivo*. They suggest that in its natural state the pigment exists in one amorphous and two crystalline forms.

The analogies between absorption spectra of artificial and natural aggregates of Chl and BChl should not be drawn without reservations; band shifts *in vivo* could result from factors other than the mutual interactions of the Chl molecules. In *Rhodopseudomonas spheroides* there are three distinct conditions under which the band at 850 mμ is reduced or eliminated and the band at 870 mμ enhanced: absence of colored carotenoids, low temperature (near 1°K), and low density of pigmentation (as in cells grown aerobically). The interpretation of these effects is confused by the fact that *Chromatium* shows an opposite pattern. The very conditions that accentuate the longest wave (870 mμ) band in *R. spheroides* act in *Chromatium* to augment the 800 mμ band at the expense of the longer wave bands.

In leaves the very first Chl *a* that is formed from protochlorophyll absorbs maximally at 684 mμ. Within minutes the maximum shifts to 673 mμ, and after a few hours the 673 and 683 mμ forms, characteristic of the mature leaf, can be detected. It is unlikely that the first few molecules of Chl formed are in a more condensed state than the pigment that accumulates later. A special linkage to protein is a more likely explanation for the 684 mμ band of the newly formed Chl.

The absorption bands of Chl and BChl *in vivo* are not much broader than their counterparts *in vitro*. Whatever the source of the broadening (exciton splitting?), it is not eliminated by reducing the temperature. For BChl *in vivo* the bands are not much sharper at 1°K than at 300°K. This applies to the bands at 375 and 590 m$\mu$, which are shifted only slightly from their locations in unimolecular solution, as well as to the strongly shifted bands at 800–870 m$\mu$.

The various infrared bands of BChl *in vivo* correspond to different types (environments) of the pigment and not to several transitions in one molecule. This is shown by the fact that the BChl types can be separated from each other. Chromatophores of *R. spheroides* or *Chromatium* are broken into smaller fragments by exposure to detergents. In some cases the absorption spectrum of a chromatophore suspension does not change appreciably when the detergent is added, but centrifugation yields two components with different spectra. All of the 870 or 890 m$\mu$ absorption resides in a sedimentable fraction, while the 850 m$\mu$ absorption remains preferentially in the supernatant fraction. The 800 m$\mu$ absorption is partitioned more or less equally between pellet and supernatant, but this BChl type can be isolated in another way. If detergent-treated chromatophores of *R. spheroides* are exposed to light and oxygen the 850 and 870 m$\mu$ BChl types are destroyed selectively. The 800 m$\mu$ type resists the photo-oxidation and becomes isolated.†

The degree of orderliness of natural Chl aggregates has been studied by several techniques. If a set of molecules has a preferred orientation in space the system will exhibit some of the optical properties of crystals: birefringence (double refraction), dichroism (polarized absorption), and polarized fluorescence. If fluorescence is excited with polarized light it will remain polarized; if excited with unpolarized light it will be polarized in the same way that the absorption is polarized.

Earlier studies by J. C. Goedheer and others showed that chloroplasts and chromatophores exhibit these effects weakly; it could not be decided whether the effects were due to orientation of the Chl molecules or to the random packing of Chl molecules in larger ordered structures such as lamellae. More definitive information has been provided by the studies of dichroism and polarized fluorescence in *Euglena* chloroplasts, reported by R. A. Olson, W. L. Butler, and W. H. Jennings, and of dichroism in spinach quantasomes, reported by K. Sauer and M. Calvin. The *Euglena* chloroplasts were observed in their natural state of orientation within the cells. The quantasomes were aligned by suspending them in a strong electric field; in the absence of the aligning field they displayed no special optical properties. In both kinds of material it was found that the absorption throughout the main part of the Chl *a* band, below about 680 m$\mu$, is unpolarized whereas the long wave absorption (680–720 m$\mu$) is markedly dichroic. Correspondingly, the fluorescence of the main Chl *a* component was found to be unpolarized, but the fluorescence at about 720 m$\mu$ showed

† The BChl type that reacts chemically at a reaction center (P870; see Section 2.1) also resists this treatment.

strong polarization. Both groups of investigators concluded that the major component of Chl *a* is disposed randomly but that a long wave component is oriented in a special way. Sauer and Calvin believe this orientation is relative to the individual quantasomes, of which there are very many in a single chloroplast lamella. The orientation inferred from the experiments of Olson *et al.* is more remarkable; the long wave Chl appears to be aligned in a special way with reference to the entire chloroplast in *Euglena* (with the porphyrin head parallel to the lamellae).

It has been suggested that all the Chl *a* is nicely oriented in these preparations but that the polarization effects could not be observed under the main absorption band for trivial reasons. Thus the fluorescence, polarized along the dipole axis that corresponds to absorption, is almost entirely reabsorbed at wavelengths where the preparation is optically dense. The small fraction that is not reabsorbed and can thus be recorded represents a component that departs in a random way from the preferred orientation. Beyond 700 m$\mu$ the preparation is so transparent that the major (polarized) component can be seen. At these wavelengths, for which the preparation is relatively transparent, the dichroic absorption is also evident. But at wavelengths for which the specimen is more opaque, the only light that is transmitted (and hence visible in the measurements of dichroism) comes through the thin edges of the chloroplasts or through smaller fragments of the quantasomes. In these edges and fragments the structure of the Chl *a* "crystal" is somewhat disorganized.

This criticism would be more cogent were it not for the fact that at 630 m$\mu$, where the preparations are about as transparent as at 690 m$\mu$, there is very little dichroism.

Also open to criticism is a suggestion that the polarized long wave component of Chl is P700. In the first place it seems unlikely that the main part of the fluorescence at 720 m$\mu$ is emitted by P700. The 720 m$\mu$ fluorescence is especially prominent at liquid nitrogen temperature; there is no evidence that it dies out during continuous illumination at this temperature. But Witt and others have shown that P700 is bleached irreversibly at low temperature. After a short period of illumination the P700 should be entirely bleached, and any fluorescence associated with the unbleached form should have vanished.

In quantasomes the amount of polarized Chl as measured by Sauer and Calvin is about ten times the amount of P700 as measured by Kok on the basis of reversible bleaching.

These criticisms could be answered by saying that only a small fraction of the P700 can be bleached at any one time. In this view the bleachable component represents about one tenth of the total P700; the whole exists in an orderly or crystalline arrangement. This crystallinity is what gives P700 its special quality of absorbing at a greater wavelength than the bulk of the Chl *a*. The P700 "crystal" not only acts as an energy sink, but it also provides for separation of charge by a mechanism of electron conduction as described in Section 9.4. At 77°K, where the bleaching of P700 appears to be irreversible, the majority of this pigment remains unbleached and can continue to emit long wave fluorescence.

The picture of a "crystal" of a dozen or so P700 molecules in a quantasome is certainly a fanciful extension of the experimental information. It seems more conservative to suggest that part of the Chl *a* falls accidentally into an orderly arrangement guided by the gross structural features of the tissue. This quasi-crystalline material absorbs at greater wavelengths than the main (randomly oriented) part of the Chl, in keeping with the behavior of artificial Chl aggregates. This adventitious long wave Chl should be in direct communication with the "real" P700 or with the photochemical apparatus of System II. Otherwise it will act as a *cul de sac* for energy and will thus impair the efficiency of photosynthesis.

The foregoing material can be summarized as follows. Chl and BChl exist *in vivo* in a condensed state. The aggregate may be two- or three-dimensional, and it may or may not be protected from water by a lipoprotein environment. The major component of Chl is probably an amorphous or random aggregate, but a minor long wave component is in an orderly arrangement. In purple bacteria a major part of the BChl aggregate may have an orderly structure. P870 can be identified as a nonfluorescent component, all of which can be bleached in the illuminated steady state.

The absorption spectra of Chl and BChl *in vivo* indicate that whether the aggregate is amorphous or crystalline, the dipole interaction is weak and electron orbitals do not overlap. Excitation energy transfer is probably restricted to the "slow" mechanism, at least in the green plants and algae. The band shifts of BChl *in vivo* are larger and a "fast" mechanism might still be entertained. Any conduction of electrons or holes in natural Chl or BChl aggregates, as well as in crystals of these pigments, must proceed by a mechanism (for example, tunneling and diffusion) that does not rely on conduction bands. These remarks about energy migration and electron conduction apply also to interactions among molecules of P700 or of P870, assuming that these are specialized components of Chl and BChl respectively. The absorption spectra of these substances, as revealed by their light-induced bleaching, differ little from the spectra of the major components of Chl and BChl.

There are two major differences between P700 and P870 that suggest different mechanisms for the trapping of excitation energy and the initiation of photochemistry. The singlet state of P700 is an energy sink relative to that of Chl *a*, but this is not so for P870 as related to BChl. These facts should be considered in terms of Figure 9.7; they could have a bearing on the relative values of $\tau_T$ and $\tau_t$ (Section 9.3) in the green plant and bacterial systems. Another difference between the behavior of P700 and P870 is that at low temperatures the light-induced oxidation is irreversible for P700 and reversible for P870. Thus the primary separation of charge (oxidation of P700 or P870 and reduction of an electron acceptor) appears to surmount an energy barrier in the case of P700, but no activation energy is involved in the back-reaction of P870 after its photo-oxidation. This reaction occurs even at 1°K.

The behavior of Chl $a$ in polar and nonpolar solvents (Chapter 8) shows striking differences that are of interest for the mechanism of photosynthesis, especially in connection with two light reactions as implicated by the red drop and enhancement phenomena. This subject will be examined in Section 13.3; for the present some correlations can be noted between Chl $a$ in vivo and the same pigment in wet or dry benzene. In wet benzene (corresponding to an aqueous environment in vivo) Chl $a$ is fluorescent; in dry benzene (representing the lipoprotein or nonaqueous environment) the pigment does not fluoresce. The Chl $a_{670}$ associated with System II (the "short wave" or "accessory pigment" system) is fluorescent and receives energy by resonance transfer from the water-soluble phycobilins. The long wave (System I) Chl $a_{680}$ is nonfluorescent† and does not receive excitation energy from phycobilins. The lipid soluble carotenes are less effective than the phycobilins in transferring energy to Chl $a_{670}$. These correlations suggest that the environments of Chl $a_{670}$ and Chl $a_{680}$ are aqueous and lipoidal respectively. P700, serving at a reaction center for the light harvesting system of Chl $a_{680}$, is probably coupled to Cyt $f$ and to an electron acceptor molecule. This reaction center could form a link between a lipoprotein region (containing Chl $a_{680}$) and one or more aqueous zones in which the chemistry of photosynthesis is continued.

The absorption spectra of Chl $a$ in wet and in dry benzene do not provide a basis for understanding the positions of the absorption maxima of the two forms of Chl $a$ in vivo. S. S. Brody has suggested that Chl $a_{670}$ is monomeric and Chl $a_{680}$ is aggregated. This could account for the fluorescence of the former and the nonfluorescence of the latter, independently of any question of aqueous and lipid environments.

## 12.2  Solid State Phenomena *In Vivo* and Their Significance

In 1951 B. L. Strehler and W. Arnold, using the firefly luminescence technique, attempted to detect photosynthetic phosphorylation in green plant tissues. A firefly extract, added to a suspension of chloroplasts that

---

† The fluorescence of Chl $a_{670}$ and the nonfluorescence of Chl $a_{680}$ are inferred from the excitation spectra for fluorescence and the related information on the roles of Systems I and II in photosynthesis (see Chapters 3 and 4).

has been illuminated, should emit light if ATP has been formed. The expected emission of light was observed, but it was also seen when no firefly extract was added. In this way Strehler and Arnold discovered delayed light emission: a luminescence of plants that can be detected minutes after excitation, that is sensitized by Chl or BChl, and that has the same spectrum as the fluorescence of Chl or BChl. Delayed light is emitted by all varieties of photosynthetic tissues.

The decay of the emission after illumination does not show a simple kinetic pattern, but very roughly the relation between emission intensity and time after excitation appears as a straight line over a wide range on a logarithmic plot (log $I$ vs. log $t$). This relationship is sketched in Figure 12.1, with the intensity of emission normalized to a value of unity for the fluorescence intensity. The fluorescence is indicated by a point at about $I = 1$, $t = 10^{-9}$ sec. Exponential decay of the fluorescence with a half-

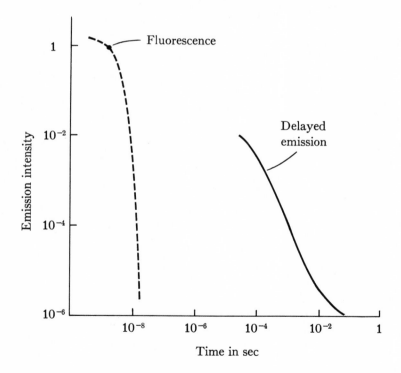

FIGURE 12.1. *Dependence of emitted light intensity on time after an exciting flash in Chlorella. The solid line represents delayed emission as measured by Arnold. The dashed curve shows the hypothetical exponential decay of fluorescence with a mean lifetime of 1.6 × 10⁻⁹ sec. The dot on this curve represents the mean lifetime measured by Brody and Rabinowitch.*

life of $1.6 \times 10^{-9}$ sec (the lifetime reported by S. S. Brody and E. Rabino-witch) is indicated by the dashed curve.

G. Tollin and collaborators found that at liquid nitrogen temperature the decay of the delayed emission is faster. The long-lived components ($>0.1$ sec) could not be detected, but the total amount of light emitted at times greater than about $10^{-3}$ sec was of the same order of magnitude at 77°K as at room temperature.

The delayed emission, having the same spectrum as fluorescence, is interpreted as resulting from the trapping of electrons in metastable states, followed by the restoration of these electrons to the singlet excited state and thence to the ground state. The distinction between fluorescence and delayed emission is then as shown in Figure 12.2. Fluorescence is

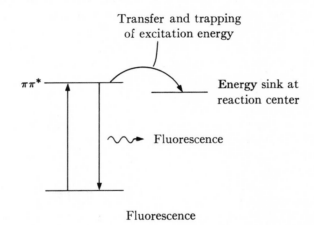

Fluorescence

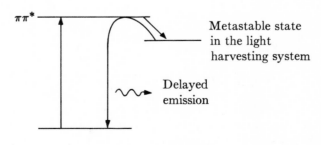

Delayed emission

FIGURE 12.2. *Possible energy pathways giving fluorescence and delayed emission in photosynthetic units.*

the emission associated with primary occupancy of the lowest singlet excited state. The decay of fluorescence follows the decay of the primary $\pi\pi^*$ excitation and is expected to be exponential. Delayed emission is a manifestation of a secondary return to the $\pi\pi^*$ level and can be expected to show complex decay kinetics. Analysis of the kinetics of delayed emission implicates a continuous range of trap depths (the trap depth is the difference in energy between the $\pi\pi^*$ level and the metastable level) rather than a unique trapping level.

The metastable states (or traps) involved in the delayed emission are not necessarily associated with a photochemical reaction center. If this metastable energy can be conducted to the reaction center, the metastable states provide a pathway for photosynthesis other than the transfer of singlet excitation energy. But if the trapped energy associated with delayed emission cannot reach the reaction center, this process represents a derailment of the flow of energy for photosynthesis.

The occurrence of delayed emission at low temperature shows that the emission does not involve a reversal of enzymatic reactions and emphasizes the electronic nature of the process. The trapping and untrapping involves interaction between the $\pi\pi^*$ level and the trapped states through small (for example, collisional or vibrational) quanta of energy. Escape from the deeper traps is relatively rare and contributes mainly to the long-lived part of the emission. At low temperature the interaction between the $\pi\pi^*$ level and the deep traps is so weak that the slower components of delayed emission are lost.

Arnold, recognizing that the delayed emission could represent photoionization accompanied by the trapping of electrons or holes, examined the electrical and optical properties of photosynthetic tissues to see if they behave like organic semiconductors. Dried chloroplasts, algae, and chromatophores do indeed show several properties of semiconductors, as listed below.

1. The electrical resistance of a film of dried chloroplasts varies with temperature in the manner of a semiconductor (for example, as described by Equation [9.4.1]). The energy gap computed from this relationship is 2.1 ev, whereas $\Delta E$ for crystalline Chl is 1.44 ev. The higher value for chloroplasts could be attributed to the fact that current must flow through the chloroplast boundaries, and it can of course be argued that Chl plays little part in this "dark" conduction.

2. Dried chloroplasts exhibit thermoluminescence. If they are illuminated and then stored in the dark for many hours, the chloroplasts are still capable of emitting light upon being heated. Analysis of the glow curves shows that a multiplicity of activation energies (trap depths) are involved in the storage of energy. This luminescence might be the same as the very slow component of delayed emission, accelerated by heating.

3. Dried chloroplasts and chromatophores exhibit photoconductivity sensitized by Chl or BChl.

4. Dried chromatophores show an abrupt increase in electric polarizability when they are illuminated with light absorbed by BChl. Apparently electrons and holes are set free to the extent that they can be separated by a weak external field. The polarizability (or dielectric constant) declines to its "dark" resting value in a few seconds after illumination.

These properties and also the delayed light emission can be described in a coordinated way as manifestations of the dissociation and recombination of electrons and holes in the Chl (or BChl) aggregate. The longer lived components of these phenomena are attributable to the trapping and untrapping of electrons; the faster components to the diffusion of electrons away from holes and their subsequent recombination. The holes are probably not trapped; they are the mobile species in most cases of organic semiconduction.

It has recently been suggested that the metastable states involved in delayed emission are triplet states, and that the return to the $\pi\pi^*$ level as well as the generation of conducting states is a result of triplet-triplet annihilation (see Section 9.4). It seems premature to assess this possibility critically, but two facts should be borne in mind. One is that it has not been possible to detect the triplet state of Chl *in vivo* (see Section 13.2). The other is that the delayed emission occurs *via* the $\pi\pi^*$ state from a manifold of metastable states having different energy levels.

The evidence for semiconduction in green plants and purple bacteria led Arnold and later Calvin to favor the idea that the photosynthetic unit operates through migration of electric charge. Singlet excited states in Chl or BChl are converted to conducting states; electrons and/or holes then migrate to the sites of photochemistry. Two variations on this idea are indicated in Figure 12.3. In the first (a) the primary excitation leads immediately and locally to dissociation of electrons and holes in the light-harvesting system. The electrons and holes then migrate separately to electron acceptor and donor sites $A$ and $D$. In the second variation (b) only a small part of the Chl ensemble can support efficient conduction. This part would correspond to the polarized component of Chl observed in quantasomes by Sauer and Calvin. Dissociation occurs at the electron acceptor sites and the holes migrate to the donor sites. This model incorporates extensive migration of excitation energy as well as conduction of charge. In the form advanced by Calvin and Tollin it was probably inspired by the electrical behavior of phthalocyanin films (Section 9.4).

When first put forward these ideas were expressed in the language of conduction and valence bands, following the treatment of conduction in

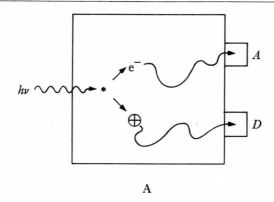

A

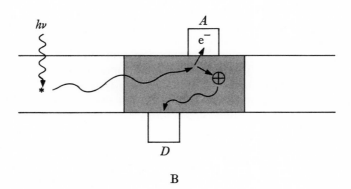

B

FIGURE 12.3.   *Hypothetical mechanisms for the operation of a photosynthetic unit through photo-ionization and the migration of electrons and holes.   A and D are electron acceptor and donor sites from which the electron transfer chemistry of photosynthesis originates.   In case (b) the energy reaches A as an exciton.   Dissociation at A generates holes that migrate to D through a small conducting part of the photosynthetic unit.*

ionic crystals and some earlier suggestions by A. Szent-Györgyi and E. Katz regarding conduction in proteins and in Chl units.   Criticism naturally arose when it became clear that conductivity in molecular crystals does not utilize conduction bands, but the role of charge migration in photosynthesis could be reformulated in terms of tunneling and diffusion of charge.   A more cogent criticism has to do with the quantum efficiency of the events that suggest ionization and conduction in photosynthetic tissues.   None of these events has been shown to reflect a major utilization of the light energy absorbed by Chl or BChl.   The quantum efficiencies of delayed emission, photoconduction, et cetera are either vanishingly small or unknown.   The available information about quantum efficiency does not rule out a major role of conducting states in photosynthesis, but it certainly does not support the idea.

If ionization facilitated by electron trapping is restricted to a small part of the Chl near a reaction center (Figure 12.3b), some manifestations of the primary photochemistry can sensibly be correlated with the manifestations of ionization and conduction.   In chromatophores, for example, one can compare the bleaching of P870, the appearance of an ESR signal, the emission of delayed light, and the light-induced polarizability.   It may be significant that all of these events show approximately the same kinetics, decaying (after illumination has ceased) in several seconds at room temperature.   At liquid nitrogen temperature the first three of these effects decay in a few milliseconds; the polarizability has not been examined at low temperature.

The quantum efficiency of P870 bleaching is at least 30%.   This bleaching has the appearance of an oxidation; it could be that P870 is the "conducting" BChl near the reaction center, the oxidation corresponding to the presence of a hole.   The experiments with pheophytinized and detergent-treated chromatophores (Section 2.1) show that all the molecules of P870 are capable of being bleached simultaneously.   This fact weighs against the possibility that P870 represents a subaggregate of BChl that is organized structurally so as to conduct holes.   Such a conducting structure should be inoperative when most of its component pigment molecules are bleached.

Still another difficulty with the conduction mechanism in photosynthesis has to do with the energy level of the conducting state.   For this state to be populated efficiently from the excited singlet state, its energy should lie a little below the $\pi\pi^*$ level.   A return from the conducting state to the $\pi\pi^*$ state then requires that an electron and a hole "find each other" and that *simultaneously* the electron acquires enough energy from its surroundings to raise it back to the $\pi\pi^*$ level.   Such a coincidence, one can argue, is too rare to account for the delayed emission.   On these grounds Franck has asserted that the conducting state is higher in energy than the excited singlet state, and can only be populated through a relatively inefficient process such as triplet-triplet annihilation or singlet-triplet interaction.

In the face of the foregoing difficulties it is not surprising that the prevailing (and more conservative) attitude is that excitation energy, and not charge, migrates to a reaction center where it becomes trapped as a localized state.   The initial photochemistry follows, and the entire sequence of events occurs without the intervention of charge migration through a set of Chl or BChl molecules. In this view ionization and conduction are aberrant processes and do not lie on the main pathway of energy flow in photosynthesis.

Delayed emission is symptomatic of ionized or other metastable states in Chl, whereas fluorescence manifests primary singlet excitation. These emissions are thus valuable indices of the events that occur in the excited pigment system, as we shall see in the ensuing sections. In particular, the emission of fluorescence shows that singlet excitation persists long enough ($10^{-9}$ sec or more) to allow extensive migration of excitation energy.

In this connection the pattern of emission sketched in Figure 12.1 is potentially of great interest. The lifetime of fluorescence in green plant tissues has been measured by Brody and Rabinowitch and again by W. L. Butler and K. H. Norris, using the pulse and phase techniques respectively. The measurements were sufficient to establish the mean lifetime, but they revealed little or nothing about the kinetics of decay. The dashed curve in Figure 12.1 shows how an exponential decay ought to look, but the experimental information offers little more than the single point on this curve. Meanwhile, the curve representing delayed emission, measured by W. Arnold to times as short as $10^{-5}$ sec, looks as if it might lead smoothly to the point that represents "fluorescence." Should this prove to be the case, it could be inferred that most of the primary excitation enters a metastable state before it can appear as emitted light. What has been called fluorescence is then actually the short-lived component of delayed emission, corresponding to rapid interaction between the singlet level and extremely shallow traps (that is, metastable states that lie barely below the singlet level).

These speculations are premature, but we are invited by the appearance of Figure 12.1 to consider the possibility that the primary excitation *in vivo* leads quickly and locally to states (for example, ionized states) other than the $\pi\pi^*$ singlet state. A wide range of possibilities can then be considered for the detailed way in which energy reaches a photochemical reaction center.

We shall end this section by considering a single experiment, due to Arnold, that is relevant to these speculations about the nature of the short-lived emission *in vivo*. It has long been known that the fluorescence of plant tissues is lost if the tissues have been heated to about 60 °C, but that heating to a greater temperature restores the fluorescence. If the yield of fluorescence is plotted against the temperature to which the material has been heated (with the heating sustained for a fixed time, say one minute), a result like that sketched in Figure 12.4 (solid curves) is obtained. Arnold has shown that the delayed emission as measured with a phosphoroscope (dashed curve in Figure 12.4) behaves like the "low

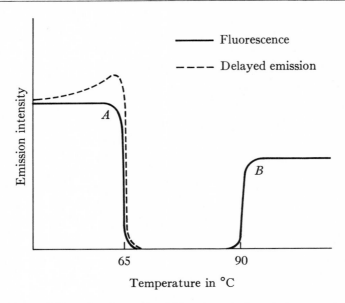

FIGURE 12.4.    *Effect of heating on the ability of green plant tissues to emit fluorescence and delayed light.    The preparation was first held at the indicated temperature for a fixed time and then returned to room temperature.    After that the light-induced emission was examined.    The solid curves pertain to fluorescence and the dashed curve to delayed emission as measured with a phosphoroscope.    The scale of the ordinate is different for the solid and dashed curves.*

temperature" fluorescence (branch $A$ of the solid curve).   The obvious interpretation is that the "fluorescence" of unheated material is a fast component of the delayed emission.   Moderate heating deranges the structure of the Chl system so as to eliminate this emission.   Stronger heating "melts" the Chl ensemble, and "true" fluorescence, corresponding to the fluorescence of Chl *in vitro* emerges.

It should not be forgotten, on the other hand, that in many ways the fluorescence and the delayed emission behave differently.   This is particularly true for the effects of poisons and other external agents on the yield and time-course of the emission.

## 12.3   The Transfer and Trapping of Excitation Energy

We have seen that the processes of photo-ionization and the diffusion of electric charge in the Chl aggregate provide a possible basis for the functioning of a photosynthetic unit.   The migration of singlet electronic excitation energy is a mechanism that seems more plausible and is certainly more popular.   Energy or charge transfer in one form or another must occur with little waste in view of the fact that photosynthetic units exist and function efficiently.

For dyes in dilute solution the transfer of excitation energy *via* excited singlet states is the only mechanism that can account satisfactorily for the fluorescence of one molecular species that results when light is absorbed by another. This kind of energy transfer remains the only sensible basis for heterogeneous sensitized fluorescence *in vivo* (for example, the fluorescence of Chl in response to the absorption of light by carotenoids), and it is the most compelling explanation for the homogeneous energy transfer (among Chl molecules) that is attested to by the operation of the photosynthetic unit.

Specific examples of energy transfer in photosynthetic tissues have been recorded many times† since T. W. Engelmann's original observation (see Section 1.1) that pigments other than Chl contribute to photosynthesis. Excitation spectra for photosynthesis and for Chl fluorescence have shown that energy absorbed by carotenoids is transferred to Chl *a* or BChl with quantum efficiencies as high as 90%; the efficiency of transfer from phycobilins and Chl *b* to Chl *a* approaches 100%.

The efficiency of homogeneous energy transfer in the Chl aggregate *in vivo* is indicated by the quantum requirements for such reactions as the oxidations of Cyt, P700, and P870. According to J. M. Olson the oxidation of Cyt in *Chromatium*, driven by light absorbed in the BChl aggregate (about 40 BChl molecules present for each molecule of Cyt), proceeds with the ideal efficiency of one electron transfer (that is, one Cyt heme oxidized) per quantum absorbed. The quantum requirements for photooxidation of P700 and P870, sensitized by Chl *a* and BChl respectively, are estimated conservatively to be 2–5 quanta per electron transfer (more recently, one quantum per electron for P700). The ratios of Chl *a* to P700, and BChl to P870, are about 300:1 and 40:1 respectively. The efficiencies of Cyt oxidation at 77°K and P870 oxidation at 1°K are comparable to the values measured at room temperature.

A possibility that must be considered in the operation of a photosynthetic unit is that the transfer of energy occurs *via* the triplet states of Chl or BChl. The molecular interactions that accompany triplet excitation are far weaker than the dipole interactions that attend singlet excitation, but the much greater lifetime of the triplet state could still allow extensive migration of energy (see Section 9.2). The transfer from accessory pigments to Chl, as shown by sensitized fluorescence, must be by way of singlet excitation; in most cases the triplet level of the excitation donor should lie below the singlet level of the acceptor. Triplet states could in principle mediate the homogeneous transfer in the Chl system and to the

† Prominent in this area have been the experiments of W. Arnold, L. R. Blinks, A. J. Dutton, L. N. M. Duysens, R. Emerson, J. C. Goedheer, C. M. Lewis, and W. M. Manning.

reaction center, but there are several reasons, to be presented in Section 13.2, for preferring the singlet exciton as an energy carrier.

The justification for accepting singlet excitation energy transfer as the light-harvesting mechanism rests on various estimates of the transfer efficiency in a photosynthetic unit. On one hand the number of individual (pairwise) transfers occurring during the singlet excitation lifetime has been inferred from observations of the depolarization and quenching of fluorescence. On the other hand the number of transfers has been predicted theoretically for the kind of Chl aggregate that seems to exist *in vivo*.

E. E. Jacobs and collaborators assumed that the increased band width of Chl *a in vivo* results from exciton splitting; they estimated that the strength of dipole interaction should allow several hundred transfers during an excitation lifetime of about $10^{-9}$ sec. This estimate is supported by the observations by W. Arnold and E. S. Meek on the depolarization of Chl *a* fluorescence in *Chlorella*. The depolarization, attributed to energy transfer in a set of randomly oriented molecules, corresponded to that of Chl *a* in a viscous solvent at a concentration of $0.1M$. At this concentration the mean separation of nearest-neighbor Chl molecules is 18 Å and according to Förster's computations the pairwise transfer time† is about $3 \times 10^{-12}$ sec. About 300 transfers should then occur in $10^{-9}$ sec.

F. W. J. Teale has determined the mean number of transfers in Chl *a in vivo* in two independent ways: by observing depolarization of fluorescence and also by observing the quenching of the fluorescence by external chemical agents. The latter method does not involve any assumption concerning the relative orientations of neighboring molecules; it yielded a value of 275 for the mean number of transfers. A comparable value was obtained from the depolarization measurements under the assumption that the Chl is oriented randomly.

The foregoing estimates are in good agreement with a careful theoretical treatment by Bay and Pearlstein, and the theoretical treatment shows that an average value of a few hundred transfers (in a "random walk") is enough to assure efficient functioning of the photosynthetic unit. Bay and Pearlstein used a delocalized (formally correct) treatment that leads to an equation for energy migration having the same form as the classical diffusion equation. All references to a localized description were made in such a way as to preserve correspondence between the localized and delocalized formulations. Numerical constants were based on two models.

---

† Use of the pairwise transfer time through a localized description of energy transfer is not correct, as was shown by Z. Bay and R. M. Pearlstein (see Section 9.2). The mean transfer time that gives correspondence with a delocalized treatment can be an order of magnitude less, and the predicted number of transfers is correspondingly greater.

First, a set of 400 Chl $a$ molecules was assumed to occupy the volume of a quantasome (an oblate spheroid 100 Å × 200 Å) in a three-dimensional aggregate. In this model the nearest-neighbor spacing is 17 Å. This can be taken as a model for the far red System I, with 400 molecules of light-harvesting Chl $a$ and a single P700 molecule as an energy sink. From the data on sensitization of Chl fluorescence, coupled with the information relevant to the red drop and enhancement effects (Sections 3.2 and 4.1), this Chl is nonfluorescent. This means that the trapping of excitation energy is so efficient that the yield of fluorescence is vanishingly small. The lifetime of the excited singlet state is correspondingly far less than the intrinsic lifetime.† The computations based on this model are fully compatible with the behavior of its counterpart in living cells. The rate of energy transfer was computed to be such that the fluorescence yield is 0.006 and the excitation lifetime is $0.9 \times 10^{-10}$ sec, corresponding to an efficiency of 99.4% for the collection of energy by the sink. If the 400 Chl molecules are deployed on the surface of the quantasome in a two-dimensional array the transfer is calculated to be even more efficient because the molecules are crowded closer together. In the three-dimensional case the mean number of transfers in a random walk is 130.

A second computation was made for a model representing the fluorescent Chl $a$ of System II (again see Sections 3.2 and 4.1). The observed yield and lifetime of fluorescence from this Chl component will be discussed in Section 13.1; very roughly the Chl $a$ of System II (which comprises about one third of the total Chl $a$) has a fluorescence yield of 0.07 and an excitation lifetime of $10^{-9}$ sec. Assuming that 100 such Chl $a$ molecules are distributed throughout the volume of a quantasome, Bay and Pearlstein computed a lifetime of $0.4 \times 10^{-9}$ sec. The transfer of energy to the hypothetical reaction center involves fifty jumps on the average and is 97% efficient; the fluorescence yield is predicted to be 0.03. This calculation seems to represent an improvement on nature; in any case it shows that the energy transfer mechanism is entirely feasible.

In the foregoing calculations it was assumed that the trapping of energy is irreversible, that is, trapping always occurs when the molecule representing the energy sink becomes excited. Aside from speculations based on the properties of P700 and P870 (see Sections 9.3 and 12.1), little is known about the mechanism of trapping. For System II in green plants and algae (the short wave, oxygen-evolving system) the nature of a reaction center is wholly obscure. But regardless of the details of the trapping process we have seen that the transfer of singlet excitation energy is completely acceptable as a basis for the collection of light energy and its delivery to photochemical reaction centers in photosynthesis.

† For Chl $a$ the intrinsic lifetime, corresponding to a fluorescence yield of 100%, is $15 \times 10^{-9}$ sec (see Section 8.1).

# 13. Excited States and Photochemistry in Chloroplasts and Chromatophores

## 13.1 The Nature and Significance of Fluorescence

FLUORESCENCE represents energy that is not used for photosynthesis; variations in the photochemical utilization of light energy are reflected by fluctuations in the intensity of fluorescence. There is a voluminous and complicated literature on this subject; it can be summarized crudely by saying that fluorescence usually rises when the absorbed light energy cannot all be used for photosynthesis. A variety of transient patterns of fluorescence intensity, occurring at the onset of illumination in green plants and algae, became more understandable when it was recognized that photosynthesis involves the interplay of two photochemical systems. By ascribing most of the fluorescence to the Chl of the shorter wave System II one can rationalize most of the complexity of the fluorescence transients and also understand how various inhibitors of photosynthesis augment the fluorescence.

The enhancement phenomenon is a synergistic action of far red and shorter wave light in promoting photosynthesis. In the case of fluorescence the opposite of enhancement has been observed in Rabinowitch's laboratory. The two qualities of light acting together evoke less fluorescence than one would expect on an additive basis.

Roughly the same effects (transients, response to metabolic inhibitors, and anti-enhancement) are seen in the delayed emission as measured with a phosphoroscope. Such observations, made for the most part by B. L. Strehler, W. Arnold, J. E. Brugger, W. F. Bertsch, and J. C. Goedheer, seem to establish a link between the delayed emission and fluorescence. This could be expected, as both kinds of emission reflect the nonutilization of excitation energy. But such similarities by no means allow the two kinds of emission to be equated, nor do they show that the excited states responsible for delayed emission are important in photosynthesis.

Direct and indirect relationships between emission and photosynthesis are shown in the following hypothetical situation. Suppose that photosynthesis utilizes the transfer of energy to a reaction center through the fluorescent $\pi\pi^*$ state of the Chl aggregate. A little diversion of this flow into metastable states in the aggregate accounts for the delayed emission. In bright light the reaction center becomes saturated and cannot trap all of the energy absorbed by the light-harvesting system; in the presence of poisons this saturation can occur also in dim light. The primary excitation, no longer drained off quickly at the reaction center, is now more likely to lead directly to fluorescence. Also a greater likelihood exists for the shunting of energy into nonfunctional metastable states and its reappearance as delayed emission.

The chief quantitative basis for a discussion of energy flow in photosynthesis is the body of knowledge about the quantum yield and lifetime of the emitted light. It will be recalled from Section 7.3 that the yield and the lifetime are in direct proportion to each other when the excited state decays exponentially, as is the case with fluorescence. As indicated in the preceding paragraph, both the yield and the lifetime of emission depend on factors that determine the efficacy of the reaction center as an energy sink. As two extreme cases we may consider Chl in dilute solution and Chl in healthy photosynthetic tissues exposed to dim light, such that the photochemical energy sink is fully effective.

As was mentioned in Section 8.1, the yield and lifetime of fluorescence of Chl *a in vitro* are 33% and $5 \times 10^{-9}$ sec respectively. These values agree perfectly with the intrinsic lifetime of $15 \times 10^{-9}$ sec (corresponding to a fluorescence yield of 100%) calculated from the integrated area under the long wave absorption band.

Careful measurements of the quantum yield of fluorescence in living algae have been made by P. Latimer and T. T. Bannister in Rabinowitch's laboratory. When extrapolated to infinitely dim exciting light a yield of 2% was obtained for *Chlorella;* other algae gave similar values. In somewhat brighter light (but below the saturating intensity for photosynthesis) the yield was found to be about 3%. By multiplying the yield by the intrinsic lifetime, one can predict an actual lifetime of $0.3 \times 10^{-9}$ sec for fluorescence in *Chlorella* exposed to dim light, and about $0.45 \times 10^{-9}$ sec in moderate light.

Actual lifetimes of the fluorescence in chloroplasts and algae have been measured by Brody and Rabinowitch, by Butler and Norris, and by Dmitrievsky. The observed values ranged from $0.6 \times 10^{-9}$ to $1.6 \times 10^{-9}$ sec for the fluorescence under moderate to bright excitation at room temperature.† These values are two to three times as great as those predicted from the yield of fluorescence, but that is just what one would expect if

---

† Bright excitation in a short flash may not saturate a reaction center and may therefore give a shorter lifetime than continuous bright excitation. Dmitrievsky reports a 2.5-fold increase in lifetime when the exciting intensity is increased fivefold in *Elodea*

the Chl *a in vivo* exists in two forms, one of them (the Chl $a_{680}$) nonfluorescent. If all of the fluorescence is associated with Chl $a_{670}$, and if this shorter wave Chl makes up one third of the total Chl *a*, the observations are mutually consistent: the yield of Chl $a_{670}$ fluorescence is 6% in dim light and 9% under moderate illumination. The lifetimes predicted from these yields are $0.9 \times 10^{-9}$ and $1.4 \times 10^{-9}$ sec respectively.

At 77°K a long wave component, centered at 730 m$\mu$, predominates in the fluorescence of chloroplasts. Butler and Norris measured its mean lifetime at $3.1 \times 10^{-9}$ sec and estimated that its quantum yield is considerably higher than that of the Chl $a_{670}$ fluorescence. The intrinsic lifetime is then close to the observed lifetime. The short intrinsic lifetime makes it unlikely that this 730 m$\mu$ emission corresponds to an $n\pi^*$ state in Chl; it should be associated with one or more of the long wave Chl components.

At room temperature the 730 m$\mu$ emission is far weaker than the main fluorescence at about 680 m$\mu$, so that the latter is represented with little error in measurements that encompass both wavelengths.

Bay and Pearlstein calculated that for 100 molecules of Chl $a_{670}$ in a photosynthetic unit the utilization of singlet excitation energy should be 97% efficient (see Section 12.3). The yield of fluorescence was predicted to be 3% and the lifetime $0.4 \times 10^{-9}$ sec. These figures are compatible with the observed values, considering the uncertainties involved both in the theoretical computation and in the experimental tests.

Let us now examine more closely the way in which the yield of fluorescence depends on the exciting light intensity. This variation has been a major point of departure in the development of Franck's theories (Section 13.3). It also has a bearing on the unresolved possibility that a fast component of delayed emission has been mistaken for fluorescence. And if interpreted correctly the fluorescence yield can give information about the photochemical utilization of energy.

In green plants and algae two characteristic intensities of the exciting light provide points of reference for discussing the variation of fluorescence yield. One is the compensation intensity, at which photosynthetic oxygen evolution is just sufficient to balance the oxygen uptake of respiration. The other, several times greater, is the saturating intensity: the intensity just sufficient to support a maximum rate of photosynthesis. A typical plot of fluorescence intensity *vs.* exciting light intensity shows changes in its slope at both of these points.

---

leaves. However, the experimental observations are not complete enough (and perhaps not precise enough) to show whether the lifetime changes systematically with the intensity of excitation. The information can be summed up by saying that the mean lifetime is about $10^{-9}$ sec and little is known about the dependence on exciting light intensity.

The dependence of fluorescence on exciting intensity shows considerable variation in different plants, but a pattern that is well-documented in *Chlorella* is the one shown in Figure 13.1. The slope of the plot of fluorescence intensity $I_f$ *vs.* exciting intensity $I_e$ increases slightly as $I_e$ passes the compensation point. The slope then remains constant until photosynthesis begins to be saturated and rises once more as saturation is exceeded. The increase in yield $(I_f/I_e)$ above saturation is approximately a doubling of the value below saturation. The doubled yield persists above saturation to considerably higher values of $I_e$; in still brighter light the slope of the curve begins to increase once more. When photosynthesis and respiration are both inhibited, as by flushing the preparation vigorously with pure $N_2$, the changes in slope at compensation and at saturation are repressed. The slope is then like that above saturation for the uninhibited preparation.

The increase in fluorescence yield at compensation can be attributed to the interplay of respiratory intermediates and photochemical oxidants. The interpretations are vague and will not be discussed further. Of much greater interest is the doubling of the yield that comes with saturation. This effect is certainly related to a saturation of the traps that capture singlet excitation energy for photochemistry. When photosynthesis is inhibited the traps are saturated and the yield has its "doubled" value even in dim light.

It is to be expected that the fluorescence yield will rise when the energy sinks cannot function. It is the factor of two that holds special interest; the nature of the problem can be seen through some simple arguments. Consider that singlet energy in the light-harvesting system can have three principal fates. It can be trapped at a photochemical reaction center, it can appear as fluorescence, or it can be dissipated without photochemical effect through radiationless de-excitations. In dim light the greater part of the energy is used photochemically, as shown by the efficiency of photosynthesis. About 3% emerges as fluorescence and probably not more than 10% is lost through radiationless dissipation. During photosynthesis the energy sink cycles between excitation and photochemically useful de-excitation. The completion of this cycle may depend on the photochemistry of photosynthesis, as in the restoration of oxidized P700 to its reduced form. In that case the sink loses its ability to accept excitation energy under light saturation or when photosynthesis is inhibited. The energy, no longer trapped, should have a far greater lifetime and the yield of fluorescence should increase by a large factor (by a factor of ten if the trapping in dim light is 90% efficient).

The relation between increased fluorescence and diminished trapping follows from a consideration of the available pathways of de-excitation. Let $f$, $d$, and $k$ be first-order rate constants for fluorescence, radiationless

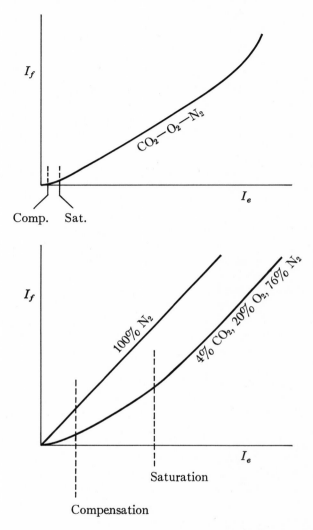

FIGURE 13.1.   *Dependence of fluorescence intensity in Chlorella on the intensity of the exciting light.   This figure is a general portrayal of the kind of behavior observed by Franck and collaborators.   The suspensions were flushed vigorously with the gas mixtures indicated on the curves.*

de-excitation (other than the useful trapping), and trapping at the photo-chemical site, respectively:

$$-dN/dt = (f + d + k)N, \qquad [13.1.1]$$

where $N$ is the number of molecules in the singlet excited state. The relative contributions of the three mechanisms of de-excitation will be in the ratio $f:d:k$. Under saturating light $k$ is zero if the photochemical trap is inoperative, while in very dim light $k$ has its greatest value $k_0$. The ratio of the fluorescence yield in very bright light to that in very dim light is

$$\frac{\phi \max}{\phi_0} = \left(\frac{f}{f+d}\right) \div \left(\frac{f}{f+d+k_0}\right) = 1 + \frac{k_0}{f+d}. \qquad [13.1.2]$$

If photochemical trapping is 90% efficient in dim light, with 10% of the excitation dissipated in fluorescence and radiationless conversions, $k_0 = 9(f + d)$ and $\phi_{max}/\phi_0 = 10$.

As another possibility the cyclic operation of the sink might continue unabated under light saturation, with dissipative events (such as the quenching of a triplet state by oxygen) taking the place of the useful photochemistry. The fluorescence yield should then be unaffected by the onset of saturation, as the sink continues to trap singlet energy. From these general considerations it is clear that a special hypothesis of some kind is needed to explain the precise doubling of fluorescence yield that is often observed.

We shall return to this problem, as approached by J. Franck, in Section 13.3. Meanwhile it must be mentioned that the pattern of fluorescence doubling sketched in Figure 13.1 for *Chlorella* is by no means universal. In chloroplasts, R. Lumry and collaborators have observed a dependence of fluorescence yield on exciting intensity that is explained quantitatively on the basis that the reaction center can accept no energy while it is engaged in photochemistry. The yield was observed to increase by a factor of about five as the light intensity passed through the saturating value for oxygen evolution. It could be concluded that in dim light about 80% of the energy is trapped usefully and the rest (aside from the small part emitted as fluorescence) is dissipated in radiationless parasitic events.

If fluorescence is actually the fast component of delayed emission, as suggested in Section 12.2 (see Figure 12.3), the foregoing arguments are submerged by other complications. Apart from any considerations of saturating the trapping center, the mean lifetime and yield of the emission are then predicted to vary with exciting light intensity in a way that depends on the specific formulation. The metastable states involved in delayed emission may be functional, giving their energy to a photochemical reaction center.   They may be parasitic, losing their energy through dissipative processes.   Finally, they may simply act as way stations, taking energy from the singlet excited state and then restoring the energy to that state.   In the third case the metastable states do not alter the yield of the emission but they do prolong its mean lifetime by detaining energy and then returning it to the emissive state.   In the first cases the yield and lifetime are both affected.   And in every case the simple proportionality between yield and lifetime, characteristic of fluorescence, is lost.

The experimental information is not yet adequate to test these ideas. Weighing against the identification of fluorescence as "fast" delayed emission is the fact that under light saturation the yield of delayed emission (measured with a phosphoroscope) is not merely doubled; it can be increased by a factor of ten or twenty.

The purple bacteria do not seem to have two functionally distinct light-harvesting systems.   They show neither the red drop and enhancement phenomena nor the chromatic transients that imply the cooperation of two photochemical reactions in photosynthesis.   The bacteria, being unable to evolve oxygen, can be kept anaerobic in the light, and the complication of respiratory activity can be avoided.   For these reasons the patterns and the interpretations of light emission should be simpler in purple bacteria than in green plants, just as they are for the light-induced absorption spectrum changes.   Historically, the experimental emphasis has been on green plants and algae; data on the yield and lifetime of fluorescence in purple bacteria are comparatively fragmentary.

The long wave absorption band of BChl *in vitro* has about the same shape and intensity as that of Chl *a*, so the intrinsic lifetime of the fluorescent state in BChl should be the same as that in Chl *a*, about $15 \times 10^{-9}$ sec. In recent measurements by A. B. Rubin and L. Osnitskaya the actual lifetimes of BChl and Chl *a in vitro* were found to be $4.7 \times 10^{-9}$ and $5.5 \times 10^{-9}$ sec respectively.   In growing cultures of *Chromatium* the BChl showed a fluorescence lifetime of $0.8 \times 10^{-9}$ to $1.0 \times 10^{-9}$ sec; the lifetime rose to twice this value in stationary-phase cultures.   These lifetimes are close to the values observed for Chl *a in vivo*.   They should correspond to a fluorescence yield of 7% in growing cultures and 13% in stationary cultures.   The actual yield of fluorescence in purple bacteria is not well-known.   E. C. Wassink reported values of 0.15% for both *Chlorella* and *Chromatium;* a reinterpretation by Duysens raised the figure to about 1%. The recent careful measurements by Latimer and Bannister gave 2% for the yield in *Chlorella* extrapolated to dim exciting light.   No corresponding measurements for *Chromatium* have been made.   It is probably safe to say that the fluorescence yield in *Chromatium* is no greater than in *Chlorella:* 2% in dim light and 3% under moderate illumination.   These figures are about fourfold less than the values predicted from the observed lifetime, and in the case of *Chromatium* there is no convenient explanation in terms of fluorescent and nonfluorescent components of the chlorophyll (as there is in *Chlorella*). All of the spectrally distinct BChl components in purple bacteria contribute with equal quantum efficiency to the fluorescence, even though the 870–890 m$\mu$ component is the only one that actually emits the light. Thus if part of the BChl *in vivo* cannot give rise to fluorescence it must have the same absorption spectrum as the remainder.

According to Franck's interpretation (Section 13.3) the fluorescence lifetime should be independent of exciting light intensity. The ratio of actual to intrinsic lifetime should be equal to the yield above light saturation; it should not be equated to the yield in dim light. In that case the observed lifetime and yield are in harmony with the intrinsic lifetime, at least for green plant tissues.

The variation of fluorescence yield with exciting intensity has been examined in *Rhodospirillum rubrum* by Vredenberg and Duysens. Their results showed a competition between fluorescence, radiationless dissipation, and trapping of energy by the trace constituent P890 (resulting in the bleaching of this pigment). The fluorescence yield could be expressed accurately by the equation

$$\frac{\phi}{\phi_0} = \frac{f + d + k_0}{f + d + k} \qquad [13.1.3]$$

(compare Equation [13.1.2]), where $f$, $d$, and $k$ are rate constants for the three competitive processes. The constant $k$ is proportional to the amount of unbleached P890; $k_0$ and $\phi_0$ pertain to the limit in very dim light. In very bright light $k$ becomes zero and Equation [13.1.3] reduces to Equation [13.1.2]. At the very start of illumination, before any P890 has become bleached, $k = k_0$ and $\phi = \phi_0$.

The data of Vredenberg and Duysens for *R. rubrum* showed $\phi_{max}/\phi_0$ to be about 2; as with *Chlorella* the fluorescence yield is approximately doubled in bright light. Then according to Equation [13.1.2],

$$k_0/(f + d) \approx 1.$$

Since the fluorescence yield is small, probably 2 % or less, $f \ll d$ and $k_0 \approx d$. This means that under the best conditions (in dim light) only about half of the absorbed light is used for bleaching P890. The prospect that the other half is wasted is not pleasing from the point of view of efficient photosynthesis. One could speculate that the radiationless process identified by the constant $d$ is actually a part of photosynthesis. Even so, these results conflict with J. M. Olson's report that the quantum efficiency for cytochrome oxidation in *Chromatium* is 100%.

Further difficulty arises through a careful examination of the kinetics of the change in fluorescence yield and the bleaching of P890. These changes begin at the onset of actinic illumination and reflect the transition from a "dark" to a "light" steady state. Superficially they follow a similar time course, as sketched in Figure 13.2. But on careful analysis in terms of Equation [13.1.3] it appears that the change in fluorescence yield progresses more rapidly than the bleaching of P890, at least in chromatophores of *R. spheroides* and *Chromatium*. In other words Equation [13.1.3] is satisfied in the steady state, but not during a transition between steady states.

While these problems await clarification new information is emerging concerning fluorescence and absorption transients in green plant tissues. W. L. Butler, L. N. M. Duysens, and J. L. Rosenberg have all reported a connection between Chl fluorescence and the absorption change designated

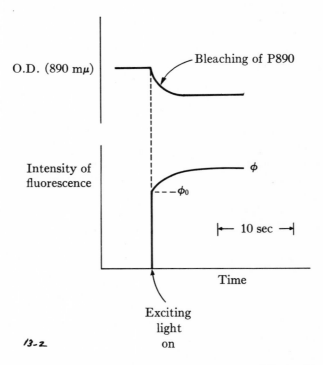

FIGURE 13.2. *Kinetics of the fluorescence intensity in Rhodospirillum rubrum at the onset of illumination, showing a rough correlation with the light-induced bleaching of P890.*

by Witt as Type 2b. The absorption change, a reversible absorption decrease at 475 m$\mu$ and increase at 515 m$\mu$, can be elicited by shorter wave (System II) excitation and is associated circumstantially with reduction of plastoquinone. The greater the development of the absorption change, the greater is the fluorescence of Chl in the steady state. Far red excitation diminishes the absorption change and quenches the fluorescence. One can imagine that the absorption change reflects a primary photochemical act in System II, possibly the transfer of an electron to PQ. When this pathway for the utilization of energy is saturated more of the primary excitation emerges as fluorescence. Far red excitation brings about oxidation of PQ so that it can engage again in the photochemistry of System II. This relieves the saturation and hence quenches the fluorescence. Hopefully, these phenomena will help to elucidate the nature of a reaction center in System II.

At present the interpretation of these observations, both with green plants and with purple bacteria, is hampered because there are too many factors that could affect the yield of the fluorescence. Even the source of the fluorescence (that is, one or another of the possible major and lesser components of Chl or BChl *in vivo*) is not perfectly clear. There is obviously a need for careful measurements of possible variations in the fluorescence lifetime, to be correlated with variations in the yield.

As to the source of the fluorescence, one can probably rule out the bacterial reaction center pigments P870 or P890. In pheophytinized chromatophores of *R. spheroides* any fluorescence from P870 should be apparent and should diminish during illumination as the P870 becomes bleached. Actually, the weak fluorescence at about 900 m$\mu$ in such chromatophores is steady under constant illumination. It can be attributed to a small residuum of light-harvesting BChl. The fluorescent component of light-harvesting BChl is that which absorbs at 870 to 890 m$\mu$. This component is often small compared with the 800 and 850 m$\mu$ components, but the latter transfer excitation energy to the former with nearly 100% efficiency. The presence of two major fractions of BChl, one able and the other unable to promote fluorescence, is unlikely in view of the high efficiency of BChl-sensitized Cyt oxidation.

In green plants and algae the shorter wave Chl $a_{670}$ is implicated as the major fluorescent pigment. The ratio of this form of Chl to the "far red" Chl $a_{680}$ can be estimated from the relative efficiencies of phycobilins and Chl $a$ in promoting fluorescence, and also from the relative contributions of Chl $a_{670}$ and Chl $b$ in mediating the enhancement phenomenon. As mentioned earlier, this ratio is about 1:3 in *Chlorella*. There remains some uncertainty as to whether the fluorescence of Chl $a_{680}$ is nil or is only somewhat less than that of Chl $a_{670}$. Also it has not been shown whether the fluorescence comes from most of the Chl $a_{670}$ or from a lesser component.   Finally, the existence of a relatively weak longer wave fluorescence shows that a minor long wave form of Chl, other than the bleachable P700, is fluorescent.

Clearly there is much to be done toward elucidating the source of the fluorescence in photosynthetic tissues.   Until this question has been settled all considerations of fluorescence yields and lifetimes involve a serious element of uncertainty.

## 13.2   The Triplet State and Photochemistry

The photochemistry of Chl *in vitro*, as outlined in Section 8.2, provides some precedent for implicating the triplet excited state in the photochemistry of photosynthesis.   The *in vitro* reactions include the kinds of electron transfer events that appear to take place at reaction centers in photosynthetic units.   A primary reaction according to Kamen and others is the oxidation of Cyt coupled with the reduction of Chl, followed by electron transfer from reduced Chl to an acceptor molecule.   This sort of reaction has a loose counterpart *in vitro* in the photoreduction of Chl by ascorbate.   The presumed transfer of an electron from P700 to an acceptor (perhaps to plastoquinone) is represented *in vitro* by the reaction studied by Tollin and Green, described as

$$\text{Chl}^* + Q \rightarrow (\text{Chl}^+ \cdot Q^-)^* \rightarrow \text{Chl}^+ + Q^-. \qquad [13.2.1]$$

If the reactions in dilute solution are governed by collisions of the reacting molecules, the mechanism is perforce one that involves a long-lived excited state of Chl.   The singlet excited state is too transitory to afford anything but a vanishingly small photochemical yield unless preformed molecular complexes are involved.   In the organized structures of photosynthetic tissues the primary reactants are probably coupled together, and the singlet excited state could lead efficiently to photochemical events without the intervention of the triplet state.   Thus, the oxidation of P700 might follow the conversion of singlet excited P700 to a charge transfer state, in analogy with the electron transfer from a dry film of phthalocyanin to an adjacent film of chloranil (Section 9.4).

These questions might be settled if Chl in its excited triplet state could be identified as a direct precursor of one of the photochemical events.   Actually there is no direct evidence for the presence of triplet Chl *in vivo*.   The long wave (755 and 885 m$\mu$) phosphorescences ascribed by Becker and collaborators to triplet Chl *a* have not been seen in photosynthetic tissues, even at the low temperature (77°K) that favors this emission *in vitro*.   The characteristic absorption spectrum of triplet Chl can be demonstrated in illuminated solutions of Chl *a*, but attempts to detect this spectrum in chloroplasts have been unsuccessful.†

Indirect evidence for triplet Chl associated with photochemistry *in vivo* has been obtained by Witt and collaborators (see Table 4.1). The spectrum of triplet Chl is discernible in denatured chloroplasts, but it is replaced in undenatured material by the "Type 1" light-induced absorbancy change. The latter, characterized by an absorption increase at 520 m$\mu$ as well as by a bleaching at 430 m$\mu$, is suppressed by paramagnetic substances such as NO. It was inferred that triplet Chl is a direct precursor of the "Type 1" reaction product. The significance of this reaction has not been established; it may have nothing to do with photosynthesis.

There is no compelling evidence, then, for the participation of triplet Chl in the photochemistry of photosynthesis, aside from the importance of this state in mediating photochemistry in dilute solutions. At the same time there is no basis for excluding triplet Chl as a photosynthetic intermediate. The photochemical utilization and alternatively the quenching of the triplet state could be so rapid as to make its detection impossible.

Granted that triplet Chl might play a role at the photochemical reaction centers, it is less likely that energy transfer in the light-harvesting Chl aggregate makes use of the triplet state. The Chl triplet could not be detected with "flash photolysis" experiments *in vivo*, implying that the triplet was not formed efficiently or was quenched rapidly. But any quenching sufficient to prevent the detection of triplet Chl should also dissipate the triplet energy before it could reach a reaction center, unless the reaction center itself provides the quenching.

Moreover if most of the singlet excitation is converted to triplet in the Chl aggregate, the yield of fluorescence should depend simply on a competition between two fates of the excited singlet state: fluorescent de-excitation and conversion to the triplet state. This competition in the aggregate should not be affected appreciably by the conditions at the reaction centers. On this basis one could not explain the increased yield that occurs when the exciting light exceeds saturation for photosynthesis.

The preceding arguments should be qualified by recent findings that energy migration *via* triplet states can be much faster than had been believed possible. The significance of these findings for the migration of triplet energy in photosynthetic units has not been analyzed critically. But as is so often the case, seemingly firm arguments might become weakened by unexpected new information.

The triplet state is undoubtedly formed with low yield in the Chl or BChl aggregates of chloroplasts and chromatophores, but is quenched

† The absence of a triplet Chl spectrum in flash-illuminated chloroplasts was reported by J. L. Rosenberg and collaborators. A search for triplet BChl in chromatophores, using comparably intense exciting light, has not been made.

efficiently by carotenoid pigments.    This can be inferred from the studies, by W. R. Sistrom and others in R. Y. Stanier's laboratory, on the behavior of a carotenoidless mutant of *Rhodopseudomonas spheroides*.    This blue-green mutant lacks the colored carotenoids of the parent (wild type) strain; instead it accumulates phytoene, a colorless polyene having only three conjugated double bonds.[†]    Under anaerobic conditions the mutant shows normal photosynthetic growth, but in the combined presence of light and oxygen it is killed, and all of its BChl is destroyed.    The destruction of the BChl results from photo-oxidation of the pigment; *in vitro* this reaction is mediated by a complex of the form $BChl^{T} \cdot O_2$ (see Section 8.2).    Caroteneless mutants of *Chlorella* show the same susceptibility to photo-oxidation.

The photo-oxidative killing and destruction of BChl has been tested in a variety of *R. spheroides* mutants having different complements of carotenoid pigments.    It has been found that carotenoids having nine or more conjugated double bonds afford good protection against these harmful effects of light and oxygen.    The protective action of zeta-carotene, with seven conjugated double bonds, is marginal and the more saturated polyenes give no protection.    Meanwhile, H. Claes and T. O. M. Nakayama have shown that carotenoids can quench the triplet state in Chl; those with nine or more conjugated double bonds compete effectively with $O_2$ as complexants of triplet Chl.    The seven-double-bonded zeta-carotene is marginally able to compete with $O_2$ in this way, and the more saturated polyenes do not interfere with the association between triplet Chl and $O_2$. Through their interaction with triplet Chl the carotenoids are able to prevent photo-oxidations and other reactions sensitized by Chl *in vitro*.[‡]

These findings indicate that potentially destructive triplet excitations occur "accidentally" in the Chl or BChl systems of photosynthetic tissues and that the principal function of the carotenoid pigments is to quench these excitations before they can be harmful.    The carotenoids are distributed throughout the light-harvesting pigment aggregate, and in their absence the entire complement of Chl or BChl can be destroyed through photo-oxidation.    The formation and quenching of triplets therefore seems to occur throughout the entire pigment system.

In addition to quenching the triplet state in Chl, the carotenoids might keep the light-harvesting system anaerobic through a harmless cycle of photo-oxidation: triplet Chl complexed with carotenoid reacts with $O_2$ to form ground state Chl and oxidized carotenoid.    The carotenoid is then restored to its reduced form by reacting with endogenous reductants.

---

† The colored carotenoids are polyenes having a conjugated system of seven or more double bonds.

‡ Refer to Section 8.2 for a fuller description of the role of carotenoids in the photochemistry of Chl *in vitro*.

Another function of carotenoids is of course the harvesting of singlet excitation energy and the transfer of this energy to Chl or BChl.

Carotenoids cannot have an indispensable function in the mechanism of photosynthesis, at least in the bacteria, because blue-green mutants of *R. spheroides*, lacking even the colorless polyenes, show normal photosynthetic growth under anerobic conditions.

The undetectability of triplet Chl *in vivo*, and the attendant inference that the triplet state does not mediate significant energy transfer in the light-harvesting system, is not surprising in view of the powerful quenching action of carotenoids. If the triplet state is to be found in any photosynthetic tissue it ought to be observable in the carotenoidless mutants of *R. spheroides*. Direct evidence for triplet BChl in these mutants, either in the form of a long wave phosphorescence or of a characteristic change in the absorption spectrum after an intense flash of light, has not yet been obtained.

Little will be added here to what has already been written concerning the mechanism of the earliest photochemical events in photosynthesis. There is some evidence that the cyclopentanone ring, present in chlorophylls *a* and *b* and in BChl, is involved in some of the photochemical activities of these substances. This ring, at the bottom of the structures shown in Appendix I, can exist in keto and enol forms as indicated in Figure 13.3. A. S. Holt and E. E. Jacobs concluded on the basis of infrared spectra that conversion to the enol form is favored by the presence of the Mg atom and of generalized bases such as water and ethanol. It was noted in Section 8.2 that the photoreduction of Chl by ascorbic acid is most rapid in pyridine-water-ethanol mixtures and is slowed if the water is replaced by $D_2O$.

To account for the specificity of Chl in photosynthesis Franck has developed rather detailed hypotheses for the primary photochemistry,

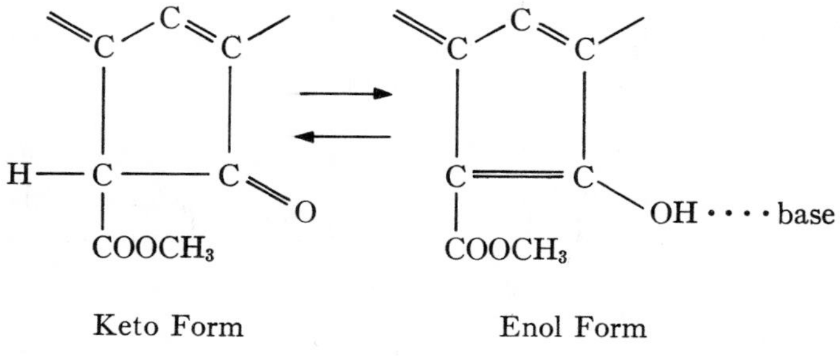

FIGURE 13.3. *Keto and enol forms of the cyclopentanone ring in the structures of Chl a, Chl b, and BChl. The enol form is favored by the presence of water, ethanol, and other generalized bases.*

involving enolization of the cyclopentanone ring of Chl and a transfer of H atoms between this ring and an adjacent molecule such as phospho-glyceric acid.   One such scheme will be examined more closely in the next section.

## 13.3   The Evolution of Franck's Theories

The theories of James Franck occupy a special position in the develop-ment of our body of knowledge concerning photosynthesis.   They have reflected the point of view of a physicist and have thus tended to deal with physical problems such as the characteristics of emitted light.   Bio-chemical developments such as the carbon reduction cycle and the func-tioning of cytochrome have not been major points of departure for these theories; rather they have been incorporated by successive modifications of the theories.   On the other side of the picture, the more biochemically oriented investigators have generated their theories from biochemical evidence and have tended to bypass some of the difficulties connected with physical theory and observation.

This is not to say that Franck holds a monopoly on sensible physical approaches to problems of photosynthesis.   His views may be regarded as a minority report that invites closer examination of some points glossed over in the more popular formulations.   The successive hypotheses put forward by Franck can be criticized on the grounds that they are over-specific and premature as unique explanations of the experimental facts. Almost every detail in these formulations can be challenged with an alternative explanation.   For the purpose of this section, anything but an uncritical exposition would become hopelessly unwieldly.   The reader is invited to supply his own alternatives and criticisms.   At the very least these ideas have great heuristic value, and the worth of an hypothesis resides largely in its tendency to stimulate further thought and investigation.

Franck's current schemes for photosynthesis in green plants and algae† originated in attempts to describe a photochemical mechanism whereby two quanta can cooperate to split water and generate a strong oxidant and a strong reductant.   These attempts have been guided by two con-straints: the photochemical specificity of Chl ought to be explained, and the observations on fluorescence should make sense.   Efforts to explain the specificity of Chl are shown in the detailed hypotheses, modified from time to time, about photochemical rearrangements of the cyclopentanone

† Franck never dealt critically with bacterial photosynthesis.   The theories described in this section pertain to photosynthesis in green plants and algae; whether these theories can be extended naturally to the photosynthetic bacteria is a question that has not been explored carefully.

ring of Chl (see later in this section). As for the fluorescence, all of Franck's formulations have incorporated an attempt to account for the doubling of the fluorescence yield that has been observed (at least in *Chlorella*) when photosynthesis is saturated or inhibited.

The doubling of the fluorescence is explained as follows. Photochemistry can begin in one of two ways; from the singlet or the triplet excited state of Chl. If the photochemistry makes direct use of singlet energy alone, it must compete effectively with fluorescence. The yield of fluorescence should be low during efficient photosynthesis and should increase by a large factor when photosynthesis is saturated so that the singlet energy is not used (recall the arguments of Section 13.1, involving Equations [13.1.1] and [13.1.2]). On the other hand if the photochemistry uses nothing but triplet energy the yield of fluorescence should be unaffected by light saturation. The emission of fluorescence is in competition with the excited singlet→triplet conversion, and this conversion will go on at the same rate whether the triplet state leads to photochemistry or not.

The observed doubling of fluorescence is too small for an all-singlet mechanism and too great for an all-triplet mechanism. It can be explained if the photochemistry involves an obligate alternation of singlet and triplet utilization at a single reaction center. Below saturation every second quantum delivered to the reaction center is used so rapidly in a reaction from the singlet state that no fluorescence is emitted. The alternate quanta are delivered to the reaction center as singlet excitation but cannot be used photochemically until the singlet state has been converted to a triplet. Fluorescent de-excitation occurs in competition with this conversion. Above saturation the "singlet" chemical reaction cannot keep pace with the influx of quanta. The singlet excitation at the reaction center is then degraded to the triplet state in every instance rather than half of the time, and the fluorescence is doubled.

The alternating use of singlet and triplet energy is depicted in Figure 13.4, together with some necessary corollary assumptions. The fluorescence is assumed to come exclusively from the "reaction center" Chl. This assumption would not be needed if the singlet level of the active Chl were part of the exciton band system of the major Chl component. But Franck maintains that the active Chl is not part of the ensemble that supports delocalized excitation; its specialized environment sets it apart so that its excitation is a localized event. Three successive steps are envisaged: first the formation of delocalized excitation in the light-harvesting system, second the capture of this energy as localized singlet excitation in the Chl of the reaction center, and finally the utilization or degradation of this localized excitation energy. If fluorescence came from the major Chl component its yield would be governed by the rate of the localizing (trap-

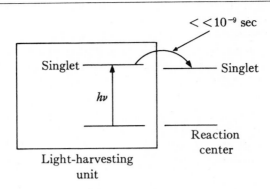

Excitation of reaction center

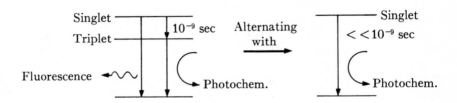

Photochemical utilization

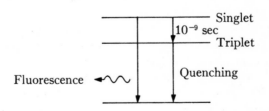

Degradation under light saturation

FIGURE 13.4. *Franck's way of accounting for the doubling of the fluorescence yield that occurs when photosynthesis is saturated. Detailed explanation in the text.*

ping) event, and the alternation of reactions shown in Figure 13.4 would not cause the required doubling.

Energy is trapped in the singlet level of the active Chl in a time small compared with $10^{-9}$ sec. This accounts for the lack of fluorescence from the major Chl component and is consistent with the calculations of Bay and Pearlstein. The fluorescence yield of about 6% above saturation corresponds to a $10^{-9}$ sec lifetime for the fluorescent state. The lower value (about 3%) below saturation is compatible with the same $10^{-9}$ sec lifetime because the active Chl is fluorescent in only half of its excitations. An explanation for the discrepancy between a 3% yield and a $10^{-9}$ sec lifetime, based on fluorescent and nonfluorescent forms of Chl (Section 13.1), is then superfluous.

The $10^{-9}$ sec lifetime of the fluorescent state is set by the rate of conversion to the triplet state; when the singlet state is used directly for photochemistry its lifetime is much less. The high rate of singlet→triplet conversion in the active Chl can be attributed to the influence of the heavy iron atom in an adjacent Cyt molecule.

At light saturation, quanta are being delivered to the reaction center at a rate of the order of one quantum every $10^{-2}$ sec (see Section 1.4). This is the time needed for a cycle of events that follows the primary photochemistry. Until the cycle is completed the photochemistry cannot happen again. The lifetime of the triplet state, whether it is determined by photochemical utilization or by dissipative (quenching) processes, is much less than $10^{-2}$ sec. Thus the active Chl is in its ground state, able to trap excitation energy, almost all of the time even when photosynthesis is saturated. In special circumstances (as in very bright light) the active Chl is prevented from being in its ground state the greater part of the time. The trapping action of the active Chl is then spoiled, fluorescence is emitted by the major Chl component, and the yield of fluorescence is more than doubled.

The specific formulations of the photochemical reactions of singlet- and triplet-excited Chl have changed from time to time. In about 1957 Franck proposed that the active Chl in its triplet state, having the character of a biradical, adsorbs an oxidant such as PGA (phosphoglyceric acid) and a reductant such as Cyt. The excited triplet state was supposed to persist until a quantum of singlet excitation could arrive at a neighboring Chl molecule. This singlet energy is used to raise the triplet Chl to a higher excited triplet state, from which the photochemistry of water splitting and oxido-reduction is driven. In this scheme the singlet reaction is sensitization of a triplet-triplet excitation, and the alternation of singlet and triplet reactions involves two neighboring Chl molecules. This scheme had to be abandoned when it was shown by Myers and French that the two photochemical reactions can cooperate even when they are separated in time by several seconds (refer to the description of "sequential" enhancement in Section 3.2). At least one of the two cooperating reactions must produce an effect that is stable for a few seconds unless acted upon in the other reaction.

In its next major form the triplet reaction was proposed to be a rearrangement in which both Chl and the primary oxidant are converted from keto to enol forms. This reaction is illustrated in Figure 13.5, with the

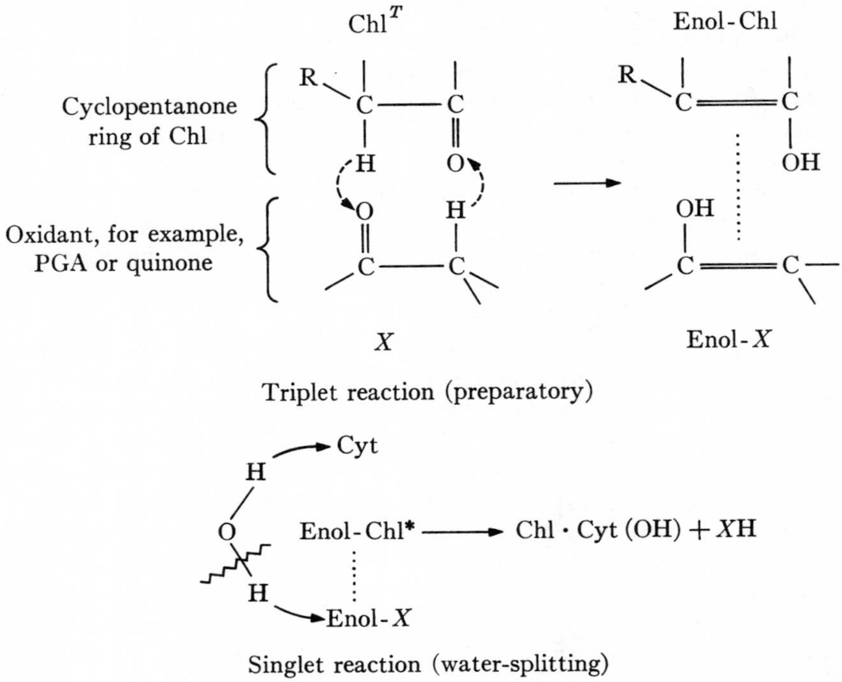

FIGURE 13.5. *Photochemistry of photosynthesis according to Franck, ca. 1959–1961. The triplet reaction is a double enolization of Chl and an oxidant X, involving mutual H transfer. In the singlet reaction water is split, Cyt is oxidized, and X is reduced.*

oxidant $(X)$ identified as PGA or perhaps a quinone. The products of this "preparatory" reaction are fairly stable and are complexed to each other. They interact, together with Cyt and water, in a singlet reaction yielding oxidized Cyt and reduced oxidant:

$$H_2O + Cyt + \text{enolized } X \xrightarrow[\left(\substack{\text{singlet-excited} \\ \text{enolized Chl}}\right)]{} Cyt(OH) + XH. \quad [13.3.1]$$

Subsequently, two molecules of $XH$ interact to give $X$ plus $XH_2$; if $X$ is PGA then $XH_2$ can be glyceraldehyde phosphate. This dismutation can be coupled to a phosphorylation, $ADP + P_i \rightarrow ATP$. The oxidized Cyt is a precursor of the evolved $O_2$.

When $X$ is identified as PGA the reaction sequence is compatible with the Calvin-Benson cycle of $CO_2$ reduction (Figure 1.5) with one reservation. Arnon and collaborators have shown that the reduction of PGA can occur in the dark at the expense of ATP and TPNH formed in a prior period of illumination. It can thus be regarded as superfluous (but not necessarily incorrect) to bring PGA into the primary photochemical mechanism. When $X$ is identified as quinone the Hill reaction with this oxidant is represented.

Still more recently, on the basis of the interpretation of light-induced absorbancy changes as listed in Section 4.1, Franck decided that both the triplet and the singlet reaction must involve oxidation and reduction. The most recent proposal is that the triplet reaction can be written

$$H_2O \cdot Chl^T \cdot Cyt + X \rightarrow Chl \cdot Cyt(OH) + XH \qquad [13.3.2]$$

followed by the dismutation

$$2XH \rightarrow X + XH_2. \qquad [13.3.3]$$

The triplet reaction is followed by a reaction from the singlet excited state,

$$Chl^* \cdot Cyt(OH) + Y \rightarrow Chl \cdot Cyt + YOH. \qquad [13.3.4]$$

Here $YOH$ is a strong oxidant, the precursor of $O_2$.

This most recent scheme bears a similarity to the series formulation for the cooperation of two completely independent photochemical systems (Sections 3.2 and 4.1). The triplet reaction generates a strong reductant, $XH$, and a weak oxidant, $Cyt(OH)$. The singlet reaction converts the weak oxidant to a strong oxidant, $YOH$. Any specific involvement of the cyclopentanone ring of Chl in the triplet reaction has not yet been formalized.

A succession of schemes to account for the red drop and enhancement phenomena has accompanied the development of photochemical models, in the framework of the postulated alternation of triplet and singlet photochemistry. The general approach has been an identification of long wave excitation with the triplet reaction alone, whereas shorter wave excitation can promote both the singlet and the triplet reactions. A recent addition to this approach is the idea that long wave excitation can lead to deleterious photochemical events that inhibit photosynthesis.

In about 1958 Franck began to develop a theory for the Emerson phenomena based on the relative positions of the singlet $n\pi^*$ and $\pi\pi^*$ levels in Chl. The major Chl component, in an environment protected from water, was taken to be like Chl in dry benzene, with the $n\pi^*$ level just a little below the $\pi\pi^*$ level. The photochemically active Chl, exposed to water, was originally compared to Chl in wet benzene, with the relative positions of the $n\pi^*$ and $\pi\pi^*$ levels reversed (see Figure 8.2). This led to difficulties which were resolved (by Franck in collaboration with J. L.

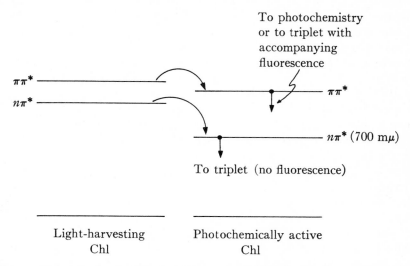

FIGURE 13.6.   *Energy levels and pathways of excitation in the photosynthetic unit according to a recent hypothesis by Franck, J. L. Rosenberg, and C. Weiss, Jr. More recently the 700 mμ absorption has been ascribed by Franck and Rosenberg to the ππ\* transition in a "crystallized" minor component of the Chl.*

Rosenberg and C. Weiss, Jr.) by assigning a lower position to the $n\pi^*$ level in the exposed Chl, as indicated in Figure 13.6.    According to this assignation the so-called P700 is actually the $n\pi^*$ transition of the photochemically active Chl.    This dramatic lowering of the $n\pi^*$ level was attributed to the proximity of a Cyt molecule.    In the highly polarized $n\pi^*$ state the excited electron of the Chl is bound to some extent by the tetrapyrrole conjugation system of the Cyt.

In the major Chl component, long wave excitation is identified as excitation into the $n\pi^*$ state.    The shorter wave excitation ($<680$ mμ) populates the $\pi\pi^*$ state.    An essential assumption must now be introduced: $\pi\pi^*$ excitation is transferred *as such* to the exposed Chl of the reaction center, and $n\pi^*$ excitation is delivered only to the $n\pi^*$ level of the exposed Chl.    Conversion of $\pi\pi^*$ to $n\pi^*$ energy in the harvesting and transferring ensemble is not allowed.    This can be made plausible if it is assumed that the Chl molecules are all coplanar and oriented so that the $\pi\pi^*$ transition dipole moments are perpendicular to the $n\pi^*$ moments in neighboring molecules.†    Granted this condition, an explanation of the Emerson phenomena follows simply and naturally.    The singlet $n\pi^*$ state

† Franck also stated (citing P. Pringsheim) that $\pi\pi^* \rightarrow n\pi^*$ conversions are delayed in molecules that are adsorbed to substrates, and suggested that the binding of Chl to lipoprotein could retard the mixing between $\pi\pi^*$ and $n\pi^*$ states.

in the exposed Chl leads directly and quickly (without accompanying fluorescence) to the $n\pi^T$ and thence to the $\pi\pi^T$ state. The triplet energy thus formed can be used for just one of the two alternating photochemical reactions. The $\pi\pi^*$ state, on the other hand, is more stable. It can drive the "singlet" photochemical reaction; it can also be degraded to the triplet state and used to drive the "triplet" reaction. Conversion of the $\pi\pi^*$ state to the triplet state is much slower than the $n\pi^* \rightarrow$ triplet conversion and is attended by the competitive emission of fluorescence. In far red light the "singlet" photochemistry is attenuated and becomes the limiting factor in photosynthesis. If shorter wave light is added, the $\pi\pi^*$ excitation affords enough "singlet" photochemistry to keep pace with the "triplet" photochemistry driven by the far red light. Thus, one accounts for the abnormally low efficiency of photosynthesis in far red light and also for the enhancing action of shorter wavelengths.

The anomalously low fluorescence sensitized by Chl *a*, in comparison with that sensitized by phycobilins, is an effect that is seen especially in the red and the blue-green algae. Franck and Rosenberg proposed that in these organisms the light-harvesting Chl molecules are not perfectly coplanar so that some mixing between $\pi\pi^*$ and $n\pi^*$ states occurs. The result is that primary $\pi\pi^*$ excitation is diverted into the nonfluorescent $n\pi^*$ state. The phycobilins, being in an aqueous environment, transfer their energy preferentially to the fluorescent $\pi\pi^*$ level of the exposed Chl.

The foregoing scheme was modified further by Franck and Rosenberg in recognition of the possibility that Chl in its $n\pi^*$ state can participate indiscriminately in reactions that would be deleterious to photosynthesis. Some of these reactions, such as

$$\text{Chl}^*\cdot\text{Cyt(OH)} \rightarrow \text{(oxidized Chl)}\cdot\text{Cyt} \rightarrow \text{Chl}\cdot\text{Cyt(OH)}, \quad [13.3.5]$$

are simply parasitic, competing with the desired photochemistry. Others, involving external oxidants such as $O_2$, can produce such combinations as (oxidized Chl)·Cyt(OH) and thereby put the photosynthetic unit out of commission until the Chl can be reduced in some way. These considerations mark a shift in the approach to the red drop and enhancement phenomena. Formerly, the inefficient use of far red light had been associated with its inability to promote one of the two cooperating light reactions. Now the emphasis has been directed toward deleterious activities following from far red illumination, and the enhancement effect is identified partly as a lessening of these inhibitory reactions (see Figure 4.3). In this view the far red light is able to drive all of the necessary photochemistry, plus some wasteful or harmful processes.

The foregoing formulations, based exclusively on the properties of $n\pi^*$ states, could not be retained in the light of new information as listed below.

These formulations remain as instructive examples of the construction of hypotheses for photosynthesis from existing physical information.

Drastic modification of the foregoing approach was necessitated by three new developments. First, it became clear that the Chl aggregate *in vivo* is almost certainly in a randomly oriented state and is not nicely arranged with mutually perpendicular $n\pi^*$ and $\pi\pi^*$ transition moments. Second, the long wave (730 m$\mu$) fluorescence as measured by Butler and Norris is too short-lived at low temperature to correspond to an $n\pi^*$ transition in the exposed Chl. Third, the long wave absorption of Chl *in vitro* is probably due not to an $n\pi^*$ transition but to the presence of dimers or polymers of Chl (see Section 8.1). The latest approach by Franck and Rosenberg was to identify the 700 m$\mu$ absorption as a consequence of small patches of crystalline Chl in some of the photosynthetic units. This crystalline Chl, or P700, has a singlet level below that of the exposed Chl, but a triplet level above the triplet level in the exposed Chl. Consequently, any singlet energy absorbed in such a unit, either by uncrystallized Chl or by P700, is unable to migrate as singlet energy to the exposed Chl. At best the energy, trapped in the singlet level of P700, can be converted to triplet energy in P700 and then transferred as such to the exposed Chl.

The reactions represented by Equations [13.3.2] and [13.3.4] are retained in this model, with the proviso that the "singlet" reaction, [13.3.4], can be driven with low efficiency by triplet excitation. The poor efficiency of triplet energy in this reaction results from a competitive process,

$$Chl^T \cdot Cyt_{ox} \rightarrow Chl_{ox} \cdot Cyt, \qquad [13.3.6]$$

which overshadows reaction [13.3.4]. This reaction, essentially the transfer of an electron from triplet Chl to oxidized Cyt, is favored because of the repulsion of the parallel electron spins in $Chl^T$. The excited electron, repelled by its partner, is driven into the conjugation system of Cyt. In singlet-excited Chl this effect is absent and reaction [13.3.6] is negligible. In summary, singlet excitation can lead efficiently to both reactions [13.3.2] and [13.3.4], but with triplet excitation the second of these reactions is highly inefficient.

The oxidized exposed Chl formed in reaction [13.3.6] may in turn oxidize an adjacent molecule of P700 within the unit, accounting for the light-induced bleaching of P700. In this way P700 can act as a substrate for excess oxidant and may sometimes protect the system against photo-oxidative injury.

In those units that lack P700, singlet excitation energy reaches the exposed Chl and both reactions [13.3.2] and [13.3.4] can proceed efficiently. In units having P700 the excitation of the exposed Chl is mainly triplet, and both the rate and the efficiency of photosynthesis are low. At this

point, to account for the enhancement phenomenon, Franck and Rosenberg introduced a second level of energy transfer: not within individual
units, but among the exposed Chl molecules of separate units.   Linked
by this long range transfer of singlet energy through the exposed Chl,
many units together comprise a "super-unit."   The units lacking P700
can then come to the rescue of those that have P700 by delivering singlet
energy directly to the exposed Chl of the latter.   In this way shorter wave
excitation, generating singlet energy in the healthy units, can enhance
the effectiveness of far red excitation, which by itself delivers only triplet
excitation to the exposed Chl of the units having P700.

By now the reader has probably gained the impression that Franck's
theories have suffered so much revision over the years that they have little
value in terms of stability and continuity.   The same can be said of the
more popular current theories (for example, the "traditional" series
formulation as outlined in Figure 4.1).   The lifetimes of Franck's specific
hypotheses are undoubtedly shortened because of Franck's characteristic
efforts to coordinate a great variety of experimental information.

# 14. Conclusion

THE FOREGOING is by no means a complete survey of the problems of photosynthesis. Many important topics have been omitted or described only sketchily. Even in the areas treated more fully, the contributions of many investigators have not been listed. These omissions can be rectified through an examination of the material listed in the bibliography.

In conclusion several points seem to be worth emphasizing. The problems of photosynthesis can yield little by little to the methods of physical theory and experimental observation, but progress is slow because of the physical complexity of the photosynthetic units. The most convincing arguments can be undermined at any moment by a startling new datum, and the experimenters continue to lead the theoreticians by the nose. It is fruitful to maintain a critical awareness of the two or more radically divergent hypotheses that usually exist for a single set of phenomena.

The very popular series formulation described in Section 4.1 is pleasingly simple and has been a nice framework for many new data, especially in the field of differential absorption spectrophotometry. But the series formulation does not deal with all the problems of photosynthesis, nor does it accommodate successfully all of the information. An awareness of other possibilities, such as those mentioned in Chapters 4 and 13, encourages a more flexible and comprehensive view of the subject.

The series formulation, with each photochemical system performing a succession of identical "one quantum → one electron transfer" acts, can be regarded as one extreme among the possible descriptions. At the other pole is a description in which a single reaction center executes a coordinated sequence of alternating photochemical acts, or even a single act involving the concerted participation of two excitation quanta of different kinds. These extremes can be driven further apart by saying that the splitting of water is part of the photochemistry in one description but not in the other, and again by framing different explanations of the Emerson phenomena (cooperation of "far red" and "shorter wave" reactions in the former case and inhibition through deleterious "far red" reactions in the latter).

192

Whether a correct description lies near one extreme or the other, or in an entirely different direction, remains to be established. Recent improvements in electro-optical instrumentation have revealed the identity and photochemistry of substances (Cyt, quinones, P700, P870, et cetera) that might constitute the reaction centers for photosynthesis. Extensive precise measurements of emission lifetimes, sorely needed for the interpretation of pathways of excitation in photosynthetic units, will surely be made in the near future. Hopefully these developments will lead to a major clarification of the early physical and photochemical events in photosynthesis.

APPENDIX I

# *Structures and Spectra of Chlorophylls*

The structures of chlorophylls *a* and *b* and bacteriochlorophyll, and also the absorption spectra of these pigments in ether, are shown in the accompanying figures.

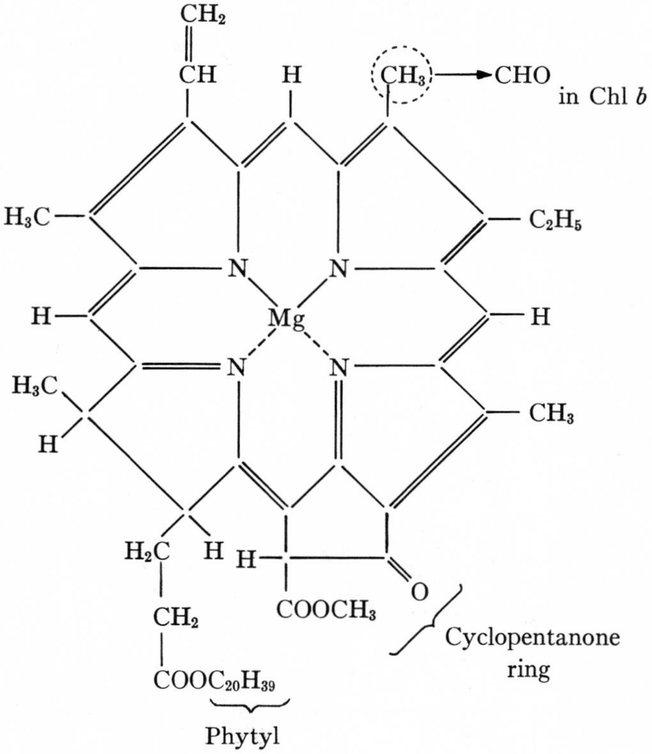


Structure of chlorophyll *a*

FIGURE A.1. *The conjugation system is in resonance with the one shown for BChl.*

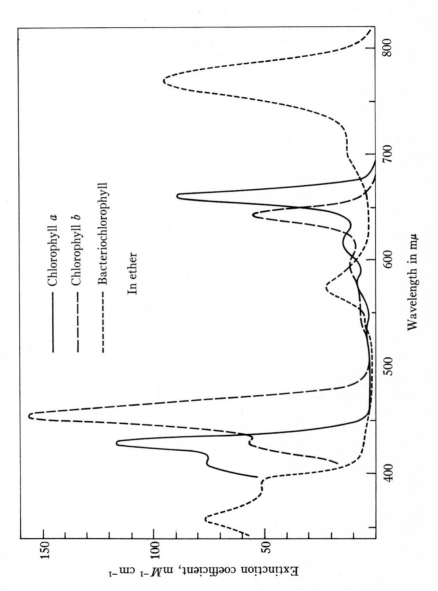

FIGURE A.2.

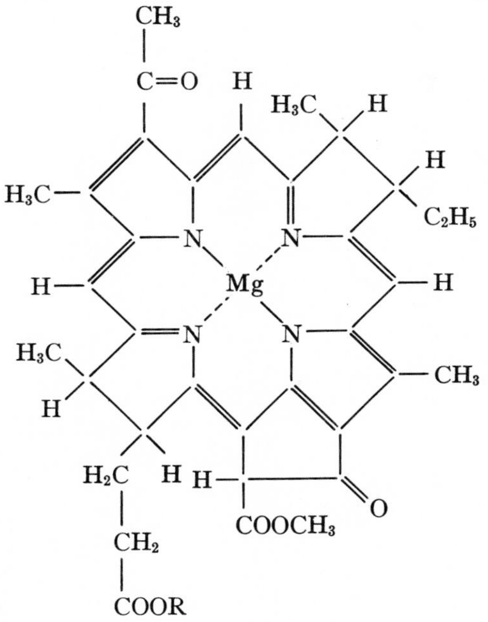

Structure of bacteriochlorophyll

FIGURE A.3.    *The group designated R has not been identified with certainty; it may be phytyl as in Chl a.*

# APPENDIX II

# Bibliography

BOOKS:

1. HILL, R., and WHITTINGHAM, C. P. *Photosynthesis.* New York: John Wiley and Sons, 1955.
2. KITTEL, C. *Introduction to Solid State Physics.* New York: John Wiley and Sons, 1953.
3. PAULING, L. *The Nature of the Chemical Bond.* (3rd ed.), Ithaca: Cornell University Press, 1960.
4. RABINOWITCH, E. *Photosynthesis and Related Processes.* (Vol. II, Part 2), New York: Interscience Publishers, 1956.
5. RICE, F. O., and TELLER, E. *The Structure of Matter.* New York: John Wiley and Sons, 1949.

REVIEWS:

1. BLINKS, L. R. "The Photosynthetic Function of Pigments Other Than Chlorophyll," *Ann. Rev. Plant Physiol.*, *5*, 93–114 (1954).
2. CLAYTON, R. K. "Photosynthesis: Primary Physical and Chemical Processes," *Ann. Rev. Plant Physiol.*, *14*, 159–180 (1963).
3. DUYSENS, L. N. M. "Energy Transformations in Photosynthesis," *Ann. Rev. Plant Physiol.*, *7*, 25–50 (1956).
4. GAFFRON, H. "Energy Storage: Photosynthesis," in *Plant Physiology* (Vol. 1B), F. C. Steward (ed.), New York: Academic Press, 1960.
5. HOCH, G., and KOK, B. "Photosynthesis," *Ann. Rev. Plant Physiol.*, *12*, 155–194 (1961).
6. McCLURE, D. S. "Spectra of Molecules and Ions in Crystals. Part 1, Molecular Crystals," *Solid State Physics*, *8*, 1–47 (1959).
7. PLATT, J. R. "Electronic Spectra of Organic Compounds," *Ann. Rev. Phys. Chem.*, *10*, 349–388 (1959).
8. SMITH, J. H. C., and FRENCH, C. S. "The Major and Accessory Pigments in Photosynthesis," *Ann. Rev. Plant Physiol.*, *14*, 181–224 (1963).
9. STANIER, R. Y. "Photosynthetic Mechanisms in Bacteria and Plants: Development of a unitary concept," *Bacteriol. Rev.*, *25*, 1–17 (1961).
10. VAN NIEL, C. B. "The Bacterial Photosyntheses and Their Importance for the General Problem of Photosynthesis," *Advances in Enzymol.*, *1*, 263–328 (1941).

11. VAN NIEL, C. B. "The Present Status of the Comparative Study of Photosynthesis," *Ann. Rev. Plant Physiol.*, *13*, 1–26 (1962).

SYMPOSIUM VOLUMES AND OTHER COMPILATIONS:

1. GEST, H., SAN PIETRO, A., and VERNON, L. P. (eds.). *Bacterial Photosynthesis.* Yellow Springs, Ohio: Antioch Press, 1964.
2. AUGENSTINE, L. G. (ed.). *Bioenergetics.* Radiation Research, Supplement 2. New York: Academic Press, 1960.
3. ALLEN, M. B. (ed.). *Comparative Biochemistry of Photoreactive Systems.* New York: Academic Press, 1960.
4. BURTON, M., *et al.* (eds.). *Comparative Effects of Radiation.* New York: John Wiley and Sons, 1960.
5. RUHLAND, W. (ed.). *Encyclopedia of Plant Physiology.* Vol. 5. Berlin: Springer-Verlag, 1960.
6. "Energy Transfer with Special Reference to Biological Systems." *Discussion of the Faraday Society*, No. 27. Aberdeen: Aberdeen University Press, Ltd., 1959.
7. KASHA, M., and PULLMAN, B. (eds.). *Horizons in Biochemistry.* New York: Academic Press, 1962.
8. McELROY, W. D., and GLASS, B. (eds.). *Light and Life.* Baltimore: The Johns Hopkins Press, 1961.
9. JOHNSON, F. H. (ed.). *Luminescence in Biological Systems.* Washington, D. C.: Amer. Assn. for the Advancement of Science, 1955.
10. KALLMAN, H. P., and SPRUCH, G. H. (eds.). *Luminescence of Organic and Inorganic Materials.* New York: John Wiley and Sons, 1962.
11. "The Photochemical Apparatus, Its Structure and Function." *Brookhaven Symposia in Biology*, No. 11. Washington, D.C.: Department of Commerce, 1959.
12. FRANCK, J., and LOOMIS, F. W. (eds.). *Photosynthesis in Plants.* Ames, Iowa: Iowa State College Press, 1949.
13. CHRISTENSEN, B. C., and BUCHMANN, B. (eds.). *Progress in Photobiology.* Amsterdam: Elsevier, 1962.
14. GAFFRON, H., *et al.* (eds.). *Research in Photosynthesis.* New York: Interscience Publishers, 1957.

# Index

## A

absorbancy transients, 20, 134
  measurement, 138
absorption spectra, 4
accessory pigments, 30
adenosine triphosphate, 8, 11
ALLEN, M. B., 45, 53
AMANN, H., 51
AMESZ, J., 50
*Anacystis*, 52
APPELL, W., 51
ARNOLD, W., 14, 16, 17, 21, 59, 96, 107, 129, 130, 156–168
ARNON, D. I., 8, 13, 14, 51, 54, 186

## B

bacteria, chemo-autotrophic, 14
  heterotrophic, 14
bacteriochlorophyll, 3, 98
  absorption spectrum, 98, 150
  aggregated, 152
  fluorescence lifetime, 174
  fluorescence yield, 174
  photo-oxidation, 180
bacteriochlorophyll *b*, 5
bacteriopheophytin, 21
BALTSCHEFFSKY, H., 27
BALTSCHEFFSKY, M., 27
BANNISTER, T. T., 103, 169, 174
BASSHAM, J. A., 11
BAY, Z., 121, 166, 170
BECKER, R. S., 99, 102, 178
BEINERT, H., 53
BENDALL, F., 50
BENSON, A. A., 11, 186
BERGERON, J. A., 52, 149, 150
BERTSCH, W. F., 168
biphotonic process, 119, 127
birefringence, 153
BISHOP, N. I., 50, 52, 53, 61

BLADERGROEN, W., 42
BLINKS, L. R., 42, 44, 165
BOGORAD, L., 150
BRODY, S. S., 98, 116, 156, 157, 163, 169
BRUGGER, J. E., 168
BURK, D., 40, 41
BUTLER, W. L., 35, 36, 153, 163, 169, 170, 176, 190

## C

CALVIN, M., 11, 24, 53, 129, 153, 154, 160, 186
carbon dioxide, reduction cycle, 186
CARIO, G., 107
carotenoids, 21, 180, 181
  photo-isomerization, 104
  and photo-oxidation, 105
  spectra, 5
CHANCE, B., 17, 27, 28, 31, 140
charge migration, 16, 106, 160
charge mobility, 127
charge transfer complex, 129
charge transfer state, 106, 122, 178
  binding energy, 123
*Chlamydomonas*, 53
*Chlorella*, 14, 15, 40, 44, 51, 55, 157, 166, 169, 171, 172, 177
Chlorobium-chlorophyll, 3, 33
chlorophyll, absorption spectrum, 97, 150, 195
  aggregated, 151
  cyclopentanone ring, 181
  dimer, 101, 116
  fluorescence, 42, 99, 168
  long wave form, 178
  monolayer, 151
  $n\pi^*$ state, 100
  phosphorescence, 99
  photochemistry, 103, 181
  photoconductivity, 129, 160
  photo-oxidation, 105
  photoreduction, 104

THIS BOOK WAS SET IN

BRUCE OLD STYLE AND WEISS TYPES

BY THE MAPLE PRESS COMPANY.

IT WAS DESIGNED BY THE STAFF OF

BLAISDELL PUBLISHING COMPANY.